D1596229

ON LIVING
IN A REVOLUTION

ON LIVING
IN A REVOLUTION

Sovell   *By*
JULIAN HUXLEY, M.A., D.Sc., F.R.S.

HARPER & BROTHERS PUBLISHERS

New York and London

This book is complete and unabridged
in contents, and is manufactured in strict
conformity with Government regulations
for saving paper.

CONTENTS

ACKNOWLEDGMENTS

The author is indebted to the following publishers for their kind permission to reprint the following copyrighted material:

Free World, Inc. for *Colonies in a Changing World*.

Fortune Magazine for *Philosophy in a World at War*.

Harper's Magazine for *On Living in a Revolution*.

Hearst Magazines Inc. for *A Biologist Finds: War Is Rare Phenomenon in Nature; Race in Europe; Thomas Henry Huxley and Julian Huxley: An Imaginative Interview* published in Town and Country.

South Atlantic Quarterly for *War: Two Jobs, Not One; Darwinism To-day; Animal Pests in Wartime*.

Tricolor for *Dr. Spooner: The Growth of a Legend*.

Yale Review for *Economic Man and Social Man*.

PREFACE

WITH two exceptions, all the essays in this volume were written and published during the course of this war. I have made some minor revisions necessitated by the passage of events. I take this opportunity of thanking the editors and proprietors of the various journals for their kind permission to reprint. I am very conscious of the fact that many of the essays reflect the circumstances of their birth, and therefore that they either "date" or (what is perhaps the same thing in another guise) have become out-of-date in this or that particular. If, in spite of this, I have decided to republish them in book form, it was because I wished to be on the record, so to speak, in however minor a capacity, in the great debate the world has been holding with itself since September, 1939.

Never, I suppose, has the process of re-thinking been so intense as in these past four years. There has been the re-thinking of old problems—the transvaluation of values; and there has been the redirection of thought to new fields —the compulsory cross-fertilization of ideas. As a result, we now live in a quite different world. There has been a revolution of thought, both reinforcing and reinforced by the revolution of economic and social fact.

The biologist inevitably recalls those drastic changes in the history of our planet to which the same term of *revolution* is applied. At least six of these geological revolutions are known to have occurred in the thousand-million-year span of terrestial life. They are essentially periods of mountain building accompanied by the emergence of more land from the sea; but they alter the whole of the environment available to living things. Just as the human revolution we are now living through has changed the world's intellectual and social climate, so they alter the world's physical

climate. As a result, at each revolutionary recurrence many
groups of animals and plants become extinct, or are reduced
to a few poor vestiges.

I have just looked up what Mr. H. G. Wells and I wrote
about the effects of these revolutions in *The Science of
Life* some fifteen years ago, and find it illuminating enough
to quote. Here it is:

> Such times, as may be imagined, are critical times for the
> world's living inhabitants. They are times both of destruc-
> tion and of progress. The specialized and the bulky and
> those that are pleasantly adapted only to the long epochs
> of smooth conditions are overtaken by disaster and
> extinguished or brought low. But their very destruction
> gives opportunity to smaller and less specialized creatures,
> which have been hardy or quick-witted enough to make
> a place for themselves in the shade of the vested interests
> of earlier life; and new adaptations are forced by necessity
> onto many survivors. So it is, that these rhythms are
> always followed not only by widespread extinction, but
> also by the rapid advance of some new and abler type of
> animal or plant machine.

There is here a remarkable analogy with what happens
in one of the historical revolutions that affect human history. The greatest difference is one of tempo. A revolution
is from one aspect a period during which the rate of
evolutionary change is markedly accelerated above the normal. But for pre-human life the general tempo is so slow
that the abnormal revolutionary rate of change is far below
the normal rate for human evolution. A geological revolution takes perhaps ten million years for its accomplishment.
The earliest known remains of the genus *homo*, not very
much on the human side of the line between ape and man,
date back only about a million years; our own particular
species of man is less than a hundred thousand years old;
and civilization began less than ten thousand years ago.
The tempo of human evolution during recorded history is
at least a hundred thousand times as rapid as that of pre-
human evolution.

The same sort of ratio holds for the abnormal speeds of
the revolutionary processes in the two fields. This has some

interesting consequences. The tempo of biological revolutions is so slow that it is out of scale with the tempo of biological reproduction and the life and death of individual plants or animals. However drastic the final effect of a geological revolution on life may be, the effect on any one generation will almost always be imperceptible. The range available to a species will contract a few miles, or the number of individuals which can support themselves in a given area in competition with their rivals will go down a per cent or so; but only very rarely will there be any cataclysmic disaster affecting large numbers simultaneously. This is as true for the Ice Age from which we have just emerged as for previous revolutions.

But in historical revolutions the rate of change is not too slow to be perceptible. The cultivated outposts of Roman civilization in Gaul awaited the westward drive of the barbarians with fascinated horror. The revolution of the Renaissance and Reformation which laid the foundations of capitalism and nationalism had the most obvious effects on every branch of life, from religion to trade, from intellectual enlightenment to daily conveniences and luxuries.

However, human evolution differs in yet another important particular from that of pre-human life. Whereas the average rate of biological evolution appears to remain constant, at least over periods that are very long even by geological standards, that of human evolution has up till now shown a general acceleration. Changes (such as inventions or improvements) of a magnitude which took perhaps fifty thousand years to accomplish in the early Paleolithic, were run through in a mere millennium toward its close; and with the advent of settled civilization, the unit of change soon became reduced to the century. But civilization, like all human tradition, is cumulative, and the rate has been progressively if irregularly speeded up during the five thousand years of written history. This speeding up has been particularly noticeable during the past three hundred years, owing to the impact of the new change-accelerating technique of modern science. Roughly and crudely, we may say that whereas at the beginning of this period the rate of new discovery and invention was such that the digestion of major change could extend over the better part of a century, it has steadily increased until the process of digestion must now be accomplished within a decade.

This is something new in history. The better part of a century is a long human lifetime, and within this span adjustment, both personal and social, is comparatively easy. When the time available for the digestion of change is reduced to a single generation, then, though individual adjustment is more of a problem, social adjustment is still not too difficult. But once the rate of major change has overtaken the rate of social reproduction, and is down to a half or a third of a generation, a new and formidable problem is introduced. The individual himself is asked to recast his ideas and his attitudes once or even twice within the space of his active working life. This applies to normal change. But during a revolutionary period the tempo is still faster, and even more basic adjustments and more rapid changes are thrust upon the world: those of us who, after beginning their careers in the golden Edwardian sunset of the Victorian day, have had to live through two world wars, know what this involves.

It is on the whole very creditable that humanity, faced with this new biological phenomenon of a speed of revolutionary change considerably higher than the speed at which the human generations succeed each other, has managed to adapt itself so well as it has. There has been a general, radical and on the whole intelligent change in outlook since 1939. On the other hand, to effect this change, a major war has been needed, and four precious years from Time's irreplaceable store. It seems clear that new machinery is required to meet the new situation properly. From now on we need to think in terms of change. This applies to all the main aspects of life, from central planning to education. Man must become consciously evolutionary, in his individual thinking, in his collective outlook, and in his social machinery.

The modern increase both in degree and rate of change emerges clearly enough if we contrast the industrial with the present revolution. During the industrial revolution the mass of the people realized only too well that a fundamental change had come over their lot, but the process was out of their hands, and indeed seemed wholly out of any control. The more prosperous section of the nation could envisage themselves as playing a part in a great historical movement, but the movement was on the whole envisaged as a long-term one, continuing on lines of more or less inevitable "progress" without alteration of its fundamental character.

But today the common man is beginning to grasp and to participate in the process of change, and the leaders of thought and action are realizing that frequent large and often qualitative changes are bound to occur in the process of change itself. Aviation, radio, television, are altering and will continue to alter the scale and the character of organized human groups. Population changes are altering the balance of power more rapidly than our parents realized. The implementation in practice even of our existing knowledge concerning diet, disease, and positive health will make sweeping alterations in effective human nature, the results of which cannot be foretold: and the results of future discoveries in glandular control, sex-determination and eugenics are still more impredictable. The techniques of large-scale over-all planning offer quite new possibilities of controlling man's physical and social environment. And as for the effects of the discoveries yet to be made in the psychological domain, involving the possibility of molding human mind and temperament almost at will, all we can say is that they are quite incalculable, but are bound themselves to be revolutionary.

The present revolution, in fact, is itself revolutionary among revolutions. For the first time the idea of the *right kind of change* has emerged, eventually to take precedence over this or that measure, this or that state of social organization, as the ultimate concern of policy.

Meanwhile there is a danger against which we must be on our guard. It is the danger of imagining that it is easy to see the goal of the revolution through which we are living.

Many people mistake their idealism for reality and their hopes for practical possibilities. This happened at the time of the French Revolution, with the idealistic assumptions about the inherent goodness of human nature once freed from kingly and priestly tyranny: the Religion of Reason failed to work, and the ideal of Liberty, Equality and Fraternity was largely sterilized by the brute facts of imperfect human and social development. It happened again in the Victorian enlightenment, with the idealistic assumptions about the inherent goodness of unrestricted economic competition: the religion of automatic progress also failed to work, and the ideal of self-help, individual enterprise, and universal educational improvement were largely sterilized by the brute facts of imperfect economic development. It happened again at the close of the last war, when the idealistic assumptions about self-determination and the League of Nations foundered on their own inherent contradictions.

At the present moment, equally unreal and often contradictory assumptions are in the air, about the sovereign virtues of socialism, of parliamentary democracy, of universal welfare for the Common Man, of military and social security, of political freedom, of federation: The complementary danger is that of over-simplification, the failure to realize the limitations of human prevision. This was particularly well exemplified in nineteenth-century economics, when the upholders of *laisser-faire* failed to foresee the inevitable growth of big business, monopoly capitalism, powerful labour and professional organizations, lobbies, and State interference, and Marx left out of his calculations the development of the "salariat" and the managerial class. Similarly in the international sphere the nineteenth-century theories of the sovereign nation failed to foresee the results of imperialism, of the filling up of the world's empty spaces

and economic frontiers, or the possibilities of the totalitarian
State and its inevitable aggressiveness.

In particular, the over-simplifiers fail to take account
of the fact that any social or economic system left to itself
is apparently bound to develop new features which eventually transform its character, and internal contradictions
which, if not attended to, lead to its violent disruption.
Once more the remedy is to think in terms of change instead
of statically or ideally. Socialism, for instance, has no blue-
print, for it is not a particular state or fixed system, but a
process. Nor is democracy to be equated with—parliamentary
democracy. It is in the most general terms a dynamic system
aimed at securing the maximum freedom and welfare and
development of the maximum number of individual human
beings. Here as elsewhere we need clear principles; but the
resulting system cannot help being an evolutionary one,
and its detailed working must be constantly supervised and
adjusted as it develops.

Thus today the lesson of our revolution is plain. It is
that we should attempt to introduce the time-dimension into
our politics and our economics, to think in terms of direction and rate of change instead of goals or blue-prints or
defined systems, however ideal.

In particular, we need the most careful analysis of the
present situation, in order that we may be able to disentangle
the fundamental from the accidental, the broad inevitable
trends of the revolution from the areas of change which are
still amenable to our guidance and control.

It is one thing to weather a gale in a sailing ship, another
to make the gale take you on your course. Civilization will
certainly come through this revolution, in spite of its violence; but if we are sufficiently wise and willing to take
enough trouble, we may make that very violence serve
constructive instead of destructive ends. When Margaret
Fuller made her pronouncement "I accept the universe,"
Emerson said "Gad, she'd better!" Today we had better
accept the revolution. Woe to those who resist it—they are
at best delaying the inevitable, at worst risking more

violence and bloodshed, in any case uselessly increasing the
frictions of the evolutionary machine and adding to the
discomforts and distresses of mankind. But woe too to those
who accept the revolution passively and imagine that its
blind forces will do all the work for them. Their last
state shall be worse than their first.

To live in a revolution is a dubious privilege, and to live
in this particular revolution is in some respects particularly
unpleasant. But it has one compensation. This revolution is
the first in which scientific knowledge and conscious planning is able to play a part. History is being made at greater
speed than ever before, and if we are willing to make the
effort, we who live in this revolution have the privilege of
helping history.

ON LIVING IN A REVOLUTION

I

THE world's most important fact is not that we are in a war, but that we are in a revolution. It is perhaps a pity that the word *revolution* has two senses—one an insurrection, a bloody uprising against constituted authority, the other a drastic and major change in the ideas and institutions which constitute the framework of human existence; yet so it is. If we like, we can use *rebellion* for the first, *historial transformation* for the second; but I prefer the word *revolution*, and shall continue to use it in what follows, with the express warning that I do not thereby mean merely barricades or bolshevism. If we once accept that statement and all its implications we find ourselves committed to the most far-reaching conclusions concerning both immediate action and future policy. From a combination of brute fact and human reason an argument emerges, proceeding as inexorably to its conclusion as a proposition of Euclid.

Let me anticipate my detailed discussion by setting down the proposition as baldly as possible. This is the sequence of its steps:

First. The war is the symptom of a world revolution, which, in some form or another, is inescapable.

Second. There are certain trends of the revolution which are inevitable. Within nations, they are toward the subordination of economic to non-economic motives; toward more planning and central control; and toward greater social integration and cultural unity and a more conscious social purpose. Between nations, they are toward a higher degree of international organization and a fuller utilization of the resources of backward countries.

Third. During the present war both military efficiency and national morale are positively correlated with the degree to which the inevitable trends of the revolution have been carried through.

Fourth. There are alternative forms which the revolution may assume. The chief alternatives depend on whether the revolution is effected in a democratic or a totalitarian way.

Fifth. The democratic alternative of achieving the revolution is the more desirable and the more permanent; the purely totalitarian method is self-defeating in the long run.

Sixth. The only universal criterion of democracy and the democratic method is the satisfaction of the needs of human individuals, their welfare, development, and active participation in social processes. A further democratic criterion, applicable in the immediate future, is equal co-operation in international organization, including the treatment of backward peoples as potential equals.

Seventh. The revolution, like the war, must be consciously accepted and deliberately entered upon. Formally, this can be accomplished by proclaiming war aims or peace aims which include the achieving of the revolution. This releases the latent dynamism of the nation and the social system.

Eighth and last. This again can be done on a democratic as well as on a totalitarian basis. By deliberately entering on the revolution in a fully democratic way it is possible to arrive at satisfactory and detailed war or peace aims which will release the powerful forces latent in the democracies, shorten the war, and, if implemented, produce a stable peace.

There is our proposition of political Euclid in skeleton form. Let us now take its bare bones and clothe them with convincing flesh and blood.

II

Point Number One was that the war is a symptom of a world revolution. Clearly the first thing to do about a revolution is to recognize it as a fact. Surprisingly enough, however, it is quite possible to ignore its existence. Just as Monsieur Jourdain in Molière's *Bourgeois Gentilhomme* discovered that he had been speaking prose all his life without knowing it, so many people to-day are beginning to discover that they have been living in a revolution without knowing it, and many others have still to discover this surprising phenomenon.

This is possible, partly because a world revolution is so vast in scope and, even though it proceeds at a rate far faster than that of history in its more normal phases, so gradual compared with the happenings of everyday life. The ordinary man sees his taxes raised, or unemployment go up, or banks crash down, or the central government extend its control, or war break out in some remote part of the globe; and he is concerned with each incident as an event in itself, not as a symptom of a larger process. It is also partly because most of us dislike radical change; after all, it is a somewhat dubious privilege to be living in anything so drastic as a revolution. Because we dislike it, we unconsciously push it away from us, begin to treat the danger as if we were ostriches, and are temporarily enabled to believe that the nasty revolution doesn't really exist.

It is worth remembering that it took us democracies a long time to recognize the existence even of the war. It is and always has been a world war, ever since its first beginnings in Manchukuo. But we refused, most of us, to admit the fact. German rearmament and the occupation of the Ruhr; Italy's attack on Abyssinia; the fighting in Spain; Munich: though some were bloodless, all were parts of a rapidly ripening world conflict. Both the fact that a world war existed and the ostrichism of our reactions to it were most obvious in the case of Spain. Here we had Franco's revolution, aided and abetted by the Axis; then Italy and Germany actively intervening, partly to secure the triumph of their side and partly to enjoy a little practice for the major struggle that they knew was to come; the Axis intervention providing counter-intervention by the Russians and the Volunteer Brigades, and undercover help from France.

And yet the democratic Great Powers persisted in building up the fiction that it was nothing but a local civil war. I remember a cartoon in a left-wing French paper—an official of the Non-Intervention Committee saying to an attendant, "Put the non-carafe on the non-table." Non-Intervention was England and France saying to each other, "Let us take non-sides in the non-war." It was the political expression of a psychological refusal to recognize an unpleasant fact—the fact that a world conflict existed. Hitler's marching into Czechoslovakia at last made Britain as a nation realize that the world war existed. I suppose it was not till his invasion of Poland that the full realization came to the United States.

It was even later that the democracies began to recognize the existence of a world revolution. This is a surprising fact, considering that it had been going on for much longer than the war. The old tribal and feudal Japan had always been totalitarian in the sense that the individual was entirely subordinated to society. The new Japan merely translated this into modern terms, with the addition of an aggressive foreign policy (in the process anticipating many of the ideas of the Nazis); but the transformation was drastic and had obvious immediate consequences. The Russian Revolution of 1917, the Turkish Revolution, the Fascist Revolution in Italy, the social and industrial transformation in Britain and other Western European democracies, the New Deal in America, the Nazi Revolution in Germany, the establishment of a dictatorship in Portugal, the revolution and counter-revolution in Spain—these, among other events, were all manifestations, sometimes total and drastic, sometimes partial and hesitant, of the world transformation that is in progress.

The Russians long ago recognized its existence, and so, in their fashion, did the Fascists, the Nazis, and the Japanese expansionists. Britain as a nation did not recognize it until much later, but when it came the recognition was explicit enough. A distinguished Swedish woman economist who spent some weeks in England in 1941 on her way to the U.S.A. told me how one night in the Savoy Hotel she found herself sitting next to a young officer in one of the Guards regiments, a typical English aristocrat. "You know," he said, "we're living in a Social Revolution here: very interesting, what?" Very interesting indeed to a representative of a class which was likely to suffer considerably as a result! The remark was a symptom. Toward the end of 1940 the adjustments of people and Government alike to the threat of invasion and to the Nazi air bombardment, together with the writings and radio talks of men like Priestley, had brought an acceptance of the fact which was both general and, on the whole, remarkably good-natured.

France had to accept the revolution, in the guise of Pétain's pale imitation of Fascism. The United States is the only great Power which has not generally recognized its existence as an inescapable fact. The proportion of its people who still imagine that after the war they can go back to the old social and international system—with a few minor differences no doubt, but essentially the same—is still high. When I was there in the winter of 1941-42 I would have said at least eighty per cent.; many American friends to whom I talked said ninety or more. Thanks to events and the writings of men like Wendell Willkie and Walter Lippmann, the proportion has been much reduced; but it is still high enough, especially as regards social and economic affairs, to prevent the emergence of a common consciousness. The most important single thing for the Americans to do now is to recognize that they, like the rest of the world, are living in a revolution, and that in some form or other it will achieve itself inevitably, whether they like it or not.

III

The next step after recognizing the existence of the revolution is to understand its nature and probable results. This can best be done by studying the trends already manifested by the revolution as it has operated in various countries, discovering what they have in common, and projecting them forward to their logical conclusion. At the outset let us be quite clear in our minds that the revolution can achieve itself in a democratic or a totalitarian way (or a mixture of the two), but that in all cases it manifests certain common tendencies. We thus can and must distinguish sharply between the inevitable aspects of the revolution and its alternative possibilities.

The inevitable aspects of the revolution are those trends which are being produced by economic and social forces entirely beyond our control. It is they that constitute the "wave of the future." But it is a plain error to equate this revolutionary "wave of the future" with Nazism or any other brand of totalitarianism. The character of the wave depends on which of the alternative methods we adopt to achieve the revolution—or, perhaps we had better say, to guide the revolution as it inevitably achieves itself. Thus dictatorship and forcible regimentation are not inevitable aspects of the revolution. Neither, we may add, is greater concern for the Common Man.

The revolution is a result of the breakdown of the nineteenth-century system, and especially of economic *laisser-faire* and political nationalism. Peter Drucker documented this in an exciting and stimulating book called *The End of Economic Man*. But he made no attempt to characterize the new system that is destined to emerge from the transformation of the old. If one must have a summary phrase, I would say that the new phase of history should be styled the Age of Social Man. Let us consider the trends of the revolution so far as it has taken place, to justify this assertion.

Within nations, in the first place, purely economic motives, though naturally they continue to be important, are being relegated to second place in favour of non-economic motives which may broadly be called social, since they concern the national society as a whole, or else the welfare of the individual considered in his relation to the society of which he forms a part.

In Nazi Germany the primary motive has been national power and prestige, to be realized through war. The complete subordination of purely economic motives can be measured by the criticisms levelled by orthodox economists against the methods adopted by Dr. Schacht. Since then the democratic countries have had to do the same sort of thing. The extent of the change can be realized when we find the May Committee reporting, only eight years before the outbreak of this war, that "democracy was in danger of suffering shipwreck on the hard rock of finance," because Britain was confronted with a budget deficit of 120 million pounds —not much more than a week of its war expenditure in 1942. To-day finance has come to be generally regarded merely as a necessary part of the machinery for realizing our aims. People are no longer asking, "How shall we pay for the war?" Instead, they are beginning to say, "If we can finance the war in this way why can't we apply similar methods on a similar scale to realizing social and cultural aims in peace?"

In Russia the subordination of the ordinary profit motive to social ends has been even more obvious. The deliberate encouragement of heavy industry under the Five Year Plan, at the expense of all other kinds of enterprise which would have flourished in a *laisser-faire* economy, is the most clear-cut example. In general, though economic efficiency is naturally insisted upon, the primary criterion for an enterprise is not whether it shall show a profit in its balance sheet, but whether it is desirable from the broad national point of view summed up in the current plan. A particular example of some interest is the expenditure on scientific research. As Bernal has pointed out in his book *The Social Function of Science,* the U.S.S.R., in spite of its low *per capita* wealth, was already before the war expending one per cent. of its national income on scientific research. Under the system of competitive private enterprise this does not "pay"; and we find that Britain (before the war) expended only one-tenth of one per cent. of its national income on science, and even the U.S.A. only sixth-tenths of one per cent.

In many other aspects of life in totalitarian countries the economic motive has been relegated to the background. I will mention only the concern with recreation. In Italy the *Dopo Lavoro* organization and in Germany the *Kraft durch freude* or "Strength through Enjoyment" did give the common man an outlet and a sense that the community was interested in him and his personal needs for a richer life: economic considerations were entirely subordinated to this. In Russia the elaborate system of rest-houses and holiday centres and the equally elaborate arrangements for holiday transport achieved the same end.

It is especially significant that similar trends have been at work in democratic countries, even when there has been no recognition of the existence of a revolution. One of the most telling examples is that of housing in Britain. It is impossible to provide the lower-income group with decent housing which shall give an economic return. Accordingly, the State has stepped in, and has given subsidies toward the building of no fewer than one and a quarter million houses or apartments in England and Wales alone during the inter-war period. The economic motive of profit has been overridden by the social motive of providing adequate living accommodation.

Nutrition offers in some ways a still more interesting example because of the progressive change to be seen. In the nineteenth century charity did its best to alleviate obvious distress. The new outlook was first expressed in Britain by the recognition that badly undernourished children could not possibly profit by education, and the consequent provision of cheap or free school meals for them. To-day the provision of free meals has been considerably extended and has been combined with the scheme for providing cheap dinners to a steadily increasing proportion of all children in State-aided schools. Free or undercost milk for children and for all expectant and nursing mothers is also being provided on a much more generous scale than before the war.

In general, the motives that have become dominant or are tending to do so are those of social security, health and housing, education and culture, recreation and amenity, and national prestige and military power; in special cases economic considerations have been overridden for almost mythological considerations, as in the Nazi persecution of the Jews as an inferior and enemy race, and the expulsion from Germany of some of the best German brains, in the interests of uncritical acceptance of orthodox Nazi doctrine.

Other apparently inevitable trends are those toward more planning and toward a greater degree of social unity or self-consciousness. The trend toward planning is so universal and obvious that little need be said on the subject. It is inevitable because, with the end of the era of primary industrial expansion, *laisser-faire* was defeating itself and unregulated private and sectional interests were coming into disastrous conflict with one another and with the common good. The trend is not merely toward more extensive planning in more fields; it is also toward a greater initiative and authority at the centre. Here again the totalitarian countries have gone farther; but the U.S.A. contains some remarkably developed examples of planning, such as the Tennessee Valley Authority, and the war has forced a planned economy on every belligerent country.

Social unity and self-consciousness perhaps demand a little more discussion. The Nazi doctrine of "Aryan" and Germanic superiority and Jewish inferiority and evil is a myth encouraging permanent and super-patriotic unity. In all totalitarian nations, and in the U.S.A. as well, the Government has encouraged art and other cultural activities on a large scale until they provide a much fuller and more intensive expression of society's awareness of itself and its ideals than in other countries. In Britain the war has produced C.E.M.A. to fill the cultural gap. In the U.S.S.R. the subsidiary nationalities have been deliberately encouraged to develop their own traditional cultures. The organized youth and health movements of the totalitarian countries and of pre-war Czechoslovakia, the fostering of the belief in a peculiar "German science," the great prestige and publicity given in Russia to scientific and geographical achievement are also symptoms of the same trend, as is the tendency to see in education not merely an intellectual, a moral, or a practical function, but a social one—the function of projecting the character, the ideals, the needs, and, in general, the social consciousness of the nation into the next generation.

In international affairs one inevitable trend is toward a higher degree of international organization. This has gone much farther in totalitarian countries—largely theoretically in Japan's "East Asian Co-Prosperity Sphere," very practically in the unification of Europe in Hitler's iron "new order." In the democratic countries it is beginning to appear under the stress of war. Lend-Lease, the leasing and sharing of strategic bases, organizations like the Middle East Supply Council, the various organizations for unified strategy and supply—these are important beginnings.

The second international trend is the greater concern with the organized exploitation of the resources, both material and human, of backward areas. This, like the first, is an inevitable outcome of that shrinking of the world to which Mr. H. G. Wells has so forcibly drawn attention. The world has become a unit, its frontiers and empty spaces are filling up.

The exploitation may be exploitation in the bad sense, like that of occupied and dominated Europe by Germany at the present moment, or like that of the mineral resources of helpless or dependent peoples by powerful foreign financial interests. Or it may be exploitation in the good sense, like the encouragement given by the United States to the political development of the Filipinos, or certain aspects of native development in British colonies like Uganda or the Gold Coast. Another symptom of the trend is the widespread talk about the need for investing very large sums in the development of backward regions, even if this be uneconomic in the short-range terms of private finance.

The logical conclusion of these various inevitable trends is a world where nations or federations put non-economic aims into first place, and exhibit a high degree of central planning, extending to every main activity of life, and a high degree of social integration in education, cultural expression, and social self-consciousness; but also a world where nations are getting tied together more closely in international organizations, and where the resources of backward areas are being more consciously exploited and developed.

IV

The third step in our proposition was that the degree to which the revolution had been achieved was in some way related to military efficiency in the war. The correlation is striking though by no means complete, and the relation appears to be a causal one, in the sense that planning, social integration, and the deliberate relegation of economic motives to second place are all essential to the successful waging of modern total war.

Here again the totalitarian countries provide the most obvious examples. Germany and Japan have been able to score their spectacular military successes because they have for years been planning for war, and because they have carried out the most drastic revolutions of their economy and social structure in the interests of that plan. The same is true of Russia: the military and technical efficiency which has surprised the world is the fruit of a deliberate and truly revolutionary plan. The lesser military efficiency of Italy has many reasons; but it is a fact that the Fascist revolution was not so thorough-going or so wholehearted as the Nazi revolution in Germany or the Communist revolution in Russia, and this fact is undoubtedly one of the causes for Italy's military failure in this war.

In other countries failure to embark upon the revolution has demonstrably impeded military efficiency. The most conspicuous example was France, where conflict as to the form the revolution should take was so acute that no agreed action was possible, and the result was disunity, disintegration of morale and national feeling, unpreparedness, and inefficiency. The inadequacy of British production and planning during the Chamberlain "phony war" period is another illustration. So is the unfortunate effect of Britain's slowness in changing her official attitude toward so-called inferior races, whether subject peoples or allies. American readers will be able to provide plenty of examples from their own country during the early months after Pearl Harbour. From an earlier period, the shipment of oil and scrap iron to Japan, the behaviour of Standard Oil and other big companies with regard to synthetic rubber and other new technical advances, and the huge output of pleasure automobiles during 1941 provide further examples of how failure to abandon the ideas of an earlier age may interfere with military efficiency when the revolutionary war eventually blasts its way in.

There will be more to say on this subject in relation to war and peace aims. Meanwhile the fact that there is a definite connection between the extent to which a country has progressed in achieving the inevitable trends of the revolution and that country's efficiency in the war, is a solemn warning to those who persist in proclaiming that the war is no time for social experiments. On the contrary, the war itself calls for the most drastic social experimentation, so drastic as to merit the term revolutionary. The only question at issue is the form which the social experiment is to take.

v

This brings us to the most interesting step in the argument, for it is here that alternatives present themselves and that the outcome may be determined by our conscious choice and deliberate effort. The revolution itself is inescapable. Even if we struggle against it we merely make the inevitable process longer, more painful, perhaps more bloody. But its form and character are not: it can be achieved in different ways, of which the alternative extremes may be described as the democratic way and the totalitarian way.

So our fifth point concerns the desirability and the efficiency of the two alternatives. We in the democracies know the undesirability of the totalitarian way. It is the way of force and domination. Inside the nation, it is employed to secure power for a small gang. It operates by means of armed force, secret police, concentration camps, the building up of irrational mass enthusiasm, the suppression of freedom of discussion, thought, and inquiry, and the persecution of contrary opinion and of scapegoat minorities. It demands disciplined uniformity and regimentation. Internationally, it imposes the domination of a chosen people or a master race, who will shoulder the burden of directing the international organization required; in return, other peoples are expected to acquiesce in remaining at a lower level of development and prosperity. In both cases, power is the primary aim, force is the primary method, and domination of the less powerful by the more powerful is the primary object.

The totalitarian method of achieving the revolution may be undesirable, but it is certainly capable of producing extreme efficiency, as the enemies of Nazi Germany have found to their cost. However, there is every reason to believe that this advantage is not lasting, and that the method is essentially a self-defeating one. It is self-defeating just because it holds its power by sheer force and can maintain itself only by constantly extending that power. But the more it extends its power the more resistance it generates both from the inside and from the outside. The question is thus not whether it will fail in the long run, but how long that run will be, and how much of civilization it will destroy in the process.

What of the democratic way? To be clear on this, the sixth step in our proposition of political Euclid, requires some hard mental effort. We may be sure in principle that it is preferable, and that it does not contain the necessary seeds of its own defeat within itself. But we must be quite sure of what we mean by democracy, sure that we are not misapplying the term or merely talking platitudes. Democracy requires rethinking in relation to the changing world. A great deal of what we have taken for granted as being of the essence of democracy turns out to be applicable only to a partial aspect of democracy or only in the particular period from which we are now escaping.

Thus it is entirely wrong to equate democracy with a system of free individual enterprise. That was the form taken

by democracy, in its economic aspects, during the period
initiated by the industrial revolution. In those conditions
that aspect of democratic freedom worked efficiently in many
ways, but also generated contradictions—for instance, by
creating economic unfreedom for large masses of the lower-
paid workers. For a different reason, it is entirely wrong to
equate democracy with representative government. That is
one aspect only of democracy, the political aspect: democracy must extend into the economic and social and all other
aspects of life if it is to be complete.

Our first problem is, then, to find a criterion or a principle
of democracy which is universal and is applicable in every
period of history, under any conceivable set of conditions.
So far as I can see, there is only one such criterion—the
individual human being, his needs and his development.
The yardstick by which we can measure democratic achievement is the satisfaction of the needs of human individuals,
and the yardstick by which we can measure democratic
method is their active and voluntary participation in all kinds
of activities. The two are in reality not separate, for participation is itself a human need to be satisfied, but for some
purposes the distinction is useful.

Under the satisfaction of needs there is to be included
not merely the provision of a reasonable standard of security
and welfare, including adequate nutrition and health, but
also equal opportunity for education, for recreation, for
freedom, and for self-development and self-expression.
Looked at from another angle, every human being born into
the world has in the eyes of true democracy a certain individual birthright—a birthright of health, strength, intelligence, varied enjoyment, and free interest, which must not
be denied or stunted if the society into which he is born
lays claim to being democratic.

Under participation there is to be included participation
in national politics and in local government and community
affairs, by discussion, through the ballot box, and by actual
service; but there is also freedom of participation in group
organizations, whether to protect particular interests (like

trade unions), or to give outlet to a shared enthusiasm (like choral societies or natural history clubs); and there is also the opportunity of participation in cultural life and in organizations for service. The technique adopted in planning schemes like the TVA or the Columbia Basin projects is demonstrating how the general public can participate in a bold central plan.

Throughout, the basic criterion is that the individual and his ultimate welfare and fullest development shall be paramount; not the State, nor national power or wealth, nor maximum profits, nor even the cultural achievements of a society in art or science or literature. And this implies the maximum amount of freedom, the fullest equality of opportunity for development, and the maximum degree of co-operation. The freedom must not be freedom at the expense of others, the opportunity must not impair the possibilities of co-operation.

The individual is the ultimate yardstick; but he cannot develop fully or freely except in an organized society. Nor is any one individual the yardstick: his freedom and opportunities must obviously be limited by the need for guaranteeing freedom from interference to his fellow-individuals.

VI

So much for the universal criterion of democracy. What remains is to find those special applications of democracy which will be necessary in the new phase upon which the world is now entering. Liberty, Equality, Fraternity—these will always constitute democracy's triple crown; but, to change the metaphor, their edges have grown blunted by use, so that they need redefining in new terms; and their particular expressions must be to a large extent determined by the social and economic conditions of the time.

The outstanding characteristic of the early nineteenth century was that it was an expanding and an industrial world. In that world democratic freedom was inevitably concerned with throwing off the shackles of the semi-fedual past, and with the rights and duties of free individual enterprise to exploit the resources of nature to the fullest possible degree; democratic equality was largely limited to political equality for the middle classes; and democratic fraternity was still largely confined to the concepts of charity and *noblesse oblige*. The outstanding characteristic of the world we are now entering upon is that it is a closed world, still organized in the form of independent nation-states, but with those states brought into constant contact and constant friction. What application of democratic principle will these conditions bring out and emphasize?

Nationalist self-determination leads, in this closed world, to competition and war; but cultural self-determination (as practised, for instance, to a notable extent in the U.S.S.R., where regional cultures are encouraged to develop fully and freely) is perhaps the best expression of Liberty in to-morrow's internationalism. The principle of Fraternity may be broadly translated as co-operation: co-operation for defense, for trade, for increased general consumption. This at once rules out punitive tariffs, purely national armies, and imperialist domination, and suggests the lines for new world-scale economic and political organizations, both international, transnational, and supernational.

In the new international sphere the most difficult of·the three democratic principles to translate into the relevant concrete terms is Equality, since at the present time the world is composed of peoples at such manifestly unequal levels of cultural and economic development. However, we find a general principle to hand in that of Potential Equality. Our aim with backward peoples will then be to raise them to a position where they can take their international place on a footing of actual equality. This does not imply that all peoples are potentially identical culturally or that there may not be real differences in innate temperament or capacity. Cultural diversity is as desirable as individual diversity. As with individuals, peoples and nations contain vast reservoirs of untapped potentiality, and the democratic approach demands in both cases that they should be provided with equality of opportunity to develop that potentiality.

We are beginning to realize the implications of these ideas in relation to China: the Chinese people must be treated on a footing of equality if the war is to be won and if we are to have a stable peace in the Far East. The same realization is dawning with regard to India. In the case of politically dependent peoples, the United States adopted the principle of potential equality in its encouragement of the Filipino's development toward independence. This was in strong contrast with the British attitude in Malaya—with appropriate results in the military sphere.

The general implications of this principle are twofold. First, a redefinition of the status of colonies and dependent peoples, with a formal pronouncement to the effect that the goal of colonial administration is preparation for self-government at the earliest possible moment. And second, a policy of large-scale development for all peoples or regions who are backward in the sense of being below standard in any aspect of life. This would not "pay" in the short-range terms of *laisser-faire* finance, but will certainly do so in the long run if our other two principles of co-operation and of freedom for cultural development are borne in mind.

VII

The final step in our argument remains—the need for entering upon our revolution consciously and of set purpose, deliberately guiding its course instead of allowing its blind forces to push and buffet our unplanned lives. The war is not merely a symptom of the world revolution; it is also one of the agencies for its accomplishment. The two are bound up together.

Our best method for achieving the revolution deliberately is through the proclamation of comprehensive war or peace aims which include the achieving of the revolution. Our enemies have long ago done this. Hitler, for instance, has included in his aims the establishment of a "new order" in

Europe, with the establishment of Germany in a dominant position as a "Master Race," and with the crushing both of bolshevism and democracy in favour of National Socialism. Japan has done the same with its slogan of Asia for the Asiatics, and its project of the "East Asia Co-Prosperity Sphere," with Japan in a similar dominant position as divinely appointed leader.

The war and peace aims of the United Nations are beginning to take more definite shape. But they could and should become both more comprehensive and more precise. For this it is not necessary that we should refer explicitly to the revolution nor envisage its complete fulfilment. But it is necessary that we take it and its implications into account.

If the revolution in some form is inevitable, and if we agree that the democratic way of carrying it out is the better way, that is the first step. The next is to make sure that we understand the inevitable trends of the revolution, and also learn how to translate the standards and methods of democracy into the new terms that the changing world demands. Then we shall have not only a body of principles to act as a touchstone, but a set of general aims to give us our direction. Our concrete schemes can then be framed in relation to those aims and checked in detail against that touchstone.

It is surprising how much assistance such a coherent body of aims and principles can give—on social security, on our treatment of subject peoples, on the role of art in the community, on international trade, and a hundred other subjects. They can also be important in warning us against possible mistakes—against a disregard of the trends of history, against every kind of undemocratic short cut to apparent efficiency, against the possible imposition of plans, however admirable, without the interest and the participation of the plannees (if I may coin a term), against every kind of narrow exploitation and racial arrogance.

It may be suggested that the best method of setting about this business is to draw up and proclaim a series of Charters, extending the general principles of the Atlantic Charter into greater detail and into various special fields. Once these were formally proclaimed by as many as possible of the United Nations there could be no going back on them; and meanwhile the experts behind the scenes could be charged with working out the practical schemes through which they would take effect. There has already been considerable talk in Britain of a Colonial Charter. A Pacific Charter might be useful to formulate the democratic point of view on the relations between the Asiatic and the white nations. A Charter of Welfare and Service would formulate the rights and duties of the individual and be in effect the charter of the common man; a Charter of Security would be the banner under which nations would be invited to co-operate in the prevention of war and aggression; and one might add a Charter of Prosperity to cover international economic cooperation, and a Charter of Peaceful Change as the first step toward the setting up of new international machinery for political adjustment.

Meanwhile it is imperative that we should be clear in our own minds as to the inescapable nature of our proposition of political Euclid. Only when we have accepted the logic of its earlier steps and fearlessly worked out their implications, can we hope to write Q.E.D. at its close by drawing the final conclusion of a set of aims which shall shorten the war, revivify the democratic nations, and lay solid foundations for peace.

ECONOMIC MAN AND SOCIAL MAN

WE LIVE in a revolutionary age. All over the world, the old types of society and the old ways of life are disintegrating. There is a race in progress between disintegration and reintegration. If disintegration wins, the result will be chaos. But if it loses, there is still a portentous alternative. Reintegration may either be on a progressive or a reactionary basis, either democratic or else openly or disguisedly Fascist. So there is another race between two radically different kinds of reintegration.

It is fairly easy to picture the society which would result from reactionary counter-revolution. All you have to do is to take the present centres of privilege and power and vested interest and imagine a tidy but despotic social order crystallizing around them. Anyhow, you have working models, admittedly different in detail from anything that could happen here, but of the same basic type, in Germany and Portugal, Spain and Vichy France.

But it is much harder to visualize a new kind of society which shall embody the new emergent social forces and yet be democratic. It is much harder just because it is so new, and there are no patterns of it yet in existence: and this very impossibility of giving a clear picture of the goal makes the goal harder of attainment.

All the same, it is necessary to try. We must try to see some of the framework of general principles needed, then to pick out what elements and what trends in our present society fit into that framework, and finally to encourage all trends which are moving in the right direction. If the new World Order just happens, it is likely to be as much disorder as order. It must be created in the light of a vision, even if the vision be but the vision of a direction, and it must be created step by painful step, and at the cost of giving up many ideas which once seemed illuminating and inspiring.

First, then, it is clear that the present is the end of an age—in Peter Drucker's words, the end of economic man. We think and believe that the new epoch of civilization will best be described as the age of social man, in which society will be much more of an organic whole, tied together mainly by the living relations of human beings and organized groups of human beings instead of mainly by the cold impersonal forces of profit and economic competition.

But it is clear that an organic society in this sense can exist on a totalitarian anti-democratic basis just as readily as on a democratic one; and so, as we believe in democracy, we must make sure that the new social order is also a democratic order. However, we also realize that, to fit in with the new framework, the expression of democracy will have to be radically transformed. Many of our old ideas must be retranslated, so to speak, into a new language. The democratic idea of freedom, for instance, must lose its nineteenth-century meaning of individual liberty in the economic sphere, and become adjusted to new conceptions of social duties and responsibilities. When a big employer talks about his democratic right to individual freedom, meaning thereby a claim to socially irresponsible control over a huge industrial concern and over the lives of tens of thousands of human beings whom it happens to employ, he is talking in a dying language. In the organic society of the future, individual liberties will mean the liberties of the individual as such—freedom of speech and opinion and belief, freedom of the person and of movement. But in his capacity as a business executive, as university president, as government administrator, a man is no longer only an individual; he incurs social obligations, and his individual freedom must be balanced against his social responsibilities.

One more general point. Every society needs its myth, its set of shared beliefs and emotionally charged ideas. It is they which give direction and support to its material organization. We must try to ensure that these vivifying concepts are based closely on concrete realities, and are neither hang-overs from an earlier age no longer relevant to the present, nor false or over-simplified abstractions. Individualism in the *laisser-faire* sense is a false abstraction which has lost any concrete relevance it once possessed; so is nationalism, in the sense of a belief in the absolute sovereign rights of separate nations. We must see that such concepts eventually die out as completely as still older ones that have now ceased to have any living relevance, like the Divine Right of Kings, or the theological view of the State, which was the basis of the medieval system. The Nazi myth of race is a false and erroneous myth: we must see that that plays as little a part as possible in the new order, not forgetting that we ourselves, in the Kipling era, went a long way toward accepting it, and that anti-Semitism and colour prejudice or colour-bars are among its manifestations. The State, as something of value in its own right, is an unreal abstraction; and when, as in Nazi Germany, it is erected into something of higher value than the individuals which compose it, it becomes a false and dangerous one.

In seeking to build a new order, we have to attempt three separate tasks, but must link them together in a single whole. First, to try to remove the elements in the old order which are working against democracy and are causing individual frustration and social disintegration; secondly, to produce arrangements which will provide security and stability, will work efficiently and will make society more of a living, organic, self-conscious whole; and thirdly, to do this on democratic principles, and to be on our guard against all anti-democratic tendencies.

The face of the future is hidden. All we can do is to try here and there to pierce the veil and to build up some picture in our mind, however fragmentary and incomplete. If such a picture expresses our human needs, and at the same time is not merely Utopian but corresponds with genuine possibilities, it will help us in our task and trend to realize itself in actuality.

Our old order contains two principles which, derived from

very different historical sources, have now combined to dead-lock progress. One is the liberal principle of economic indi-vidualism and the sacredness of the profit motive; the other is the conservative principle of class privilege based on property and on social position. In a society based on these principles, social services are considered as a mixture of charity and of palliatives designed to patch up defects in the system. The duties of the more fortunate are thought of in terms of alms-giving and *noblesse oblige* rather than of responsibility in service. For the most part, the individual human beings or the groups that go to make up the nation are tied together by impersonal bonds such as the economic motive, not by a living framework of social rights and duties.

Meanwhile, powerful monopolies develop, which, from being merely non-social, may become definitely anti-social. In the rough-and-tumble of competing interests, planning for the benefit of the community at large is all but impos-sible, and towns and cities grow up which make life uglier and more difficult instead of fuller, richer, and more beautiful. Consumers, being unorganized and without the force of the profit motive behind them, find their interests neglected as against those of producers and distributors. Law, while liberal as regards individual freedom and civil liberties, remains extremely conservative as regards property; and on the whole property rights are allowed to override human needs. In general, society fails to achieve corporate expression and individuals tend to become reduced to the level of social atoms (and frustrated atoms at that), instead of finding themselves as members of some greater whole.

How can this disintegrating system be reintegrated on a new basis? One way of beginning to rethink our social frame-work is to look at the different kinds and levels of real units that go to make up society, and then to see what claims each kind of unit has on society, and what responsibilities it should undertake.

First, then, society is not simply a mass of individuals. It consists of more or less sharply defined groups: and these groups are on different levels of size and complexity. They

are also of different kinds. Some groups are geographical,
consisting of all the people in a certain area. Others are
functional, consisting of people grouped together for some
particular purpose. And these functional groups are of two
main kinds—those concerned with material ends and practical interests, like manufacture, or trade, or law, or medicine;
and those concerned with ends in themselves, like sport
or recreation, music or art, knowledge or worship. Of course
the two kinds cut across each other and may be mixed up,
but the distinction is a real one—a shop or a factory or a
trade union is different in kind from a football club, a
church congregation, or a scientific society.

Since all groups consist of individual human beings, the
individual is our basic social unit. Next above the individual
comes the family. Above the family comes the local community or neighbourhood, in which personal relationships
play a major part. Above this level we get a change of quality:
in more extensive units, personal relationships are largely
replaced by abstract or symbolic ones. We have cities and
regions as groups of local communities; the groups of regions
that we call nations; and above this again are the as yet very
shadowy international organizations or groupings of nations.
Functional groups also fall into the same kind of categories.
All the trade unionists in a given factory make a neighbourhood group; and above them there are regional, national,
and international trade union organizations. So with
churches, businesses, political parties: though in some cases
the most extensive groupings are absent.

A group may be highly organized on one level, feebly on
another; and different kinds of groups may differ in this
respect. Politically, the nation is the most highly organized
geographical group, the region the least organized. Various
trade unions, on the other hand, are strongest on the regional
level. In our suburbs, the geographical neighbourhood
group is feeble; while in functional groups for self-expression, like choirs or dramatic societies, the neighbourhood level
often has the most vigorous organization.

The problem would seem to be this. In an organic society,

every individual and every group should have some claims
upon society and some responsibilities toward it. But too
often claims which are valid on one level have been transferred, quite erroneously, to another level. Thus individual
liberty has a very definite meaning for human beings in their
capacity as individuals and needs to be safeguarded as one
of the guarantees of democracy. But when Mr. Henry Ford,
for instance, says that the principle of individual freedom
gives him the right to do what he likes with his business, he
is confusing the issue. He is now dealing with a large and
powerful group, in which social relations ought to be the
overruling consideration—relations of the management to
the thousands of workmen employed, of the firm as a whole
to the national economy, to regional and local planning,
and so on.

Too often, again, sectional groups have allowed material
interests to override all other considerations, until they have
become quite anti-social. Big corporations whose "duty"
to make profits impels them to encourage trade with countries that are piling up armaments obviously aimed at their
own countries; firms which deliberately employ sweated
labour or refuse to install safety devices; city administrations
which permit vice and racketeering for the sake of graft—
those are a few obvious examples.

In building our New Order, groups must be made to fit in
to the social framework. Sectional economic groups cannot
be permitted to allow their "responsibility to their shareholders"—in plain English, their desire to secure maximum
profits—to override all other responsibilities. Here, much can
be done by legislation. Responsibilities toward employees can
be imposed by regulations on space and light and ventila-
tion, minimum wages, holidays with pay, recognition of
trade unions, prohibition of child labour, and so forth.
Responsibilities to the nation can be imposed by insisting
on membership of national organizations representing the
industry as a whole and subject to general governmental
supervision; through taxation or through limitation or profits
(as, for instance, in the London Passenger Transport Board

—though here the rate was undoubtedly fixed too high).
Responsibilities to the local or regional community can be
imposed through planning regulations, compulsory anti-
smoke legislation, and the like; as a war measure, local
responsibility has already been enforced as regards the
compulsory provision of fire-watchers.

It may well be that, with the passage of time, group
organizations, whether commercial firms or public bodies,
will take over various responsibilities for the housing, education, and leisure activities of their employees (as has already
been done by a few public-spirited and far-sighted firms),
and for the beautification of their neighbourhood.

In any case, social organizations of every sort and at every
level must be worked out in new terms—first and foremost in terms of people, of human well-being and possibilities of personal development, instead of in terms of abstractions like the State, or Freedom, or in purely material terms
like property and profit. A manufacturing firm is not merely
an instrument for making profit for its shareholders, or even
for turning out efficient goods. It is also a collection of
human beings, from workmen up to general manager; and it
is also part of a local community, where it can affect the lives
of other human beings in all kinds of ways—how and where
it builds its buildings; whether it discharges poisonous wastes
into the waters and clouds of grime and smoke into the air,
or whether it provides housing and recreation for its work-
people.

Again, an army is not only a military machine. It contains
tens of thousands of individuals, whose development as
human beings and as citizens it can make or mar by its
discipline and by the education it provides or fails to provide.
It is also a part of society, and can be made useful, when
not engaged in fighting, in many social tasks, as the Pioneer
Corps did in clearing up bomb damage in London or as our
soldiers, following the long-standing practice of the Russian
Army, have done in helping with the harvests.

This humanizing and socializing of sectional groups is one
way in which the new social order will differ from the old.

Another, we can be pretty sure, is the insistence that will be laid on service to the community.

The urge to be useful is a normal part of the human make-up. The service organizations like the Women's Voluntary Service or the various Youth Service Corps, which are providing outlets for service in relation to the needs of war, are demonstrating the strength of this urge. It is both probable and desirable that some form of National Service will continue after the war is over; but it will also be more difficult to organize it in peace-time. However, there is no reason to suppose that peace-time national service cannot be organized in a way which is both satisfying and also democratic. Even plain military conscription can be a democratic and educative force, as is the case in Switzerland. And there are plenty of other forms of service besides military service. We can be pretty sure that the Youth Service Corps and the Women's Voluntary Service will continue in some guise or other. If we are imaginative enough, we can give young people a choice between various types of national service—for boys, in military training, in engineering workshops, or in the fishing fleet; for girls, in domestic service, help in hospitals, communal feeding centres, crèches or welfare centres; for both sexes, on the land and on public works; for a picked élite, in youth leadership, in assistance in research, in providing entertainment in the socialized entertainment and recreation service of the future. The Civilian Conservation Corps (C.C.C.) in the United States, though designed to relieve juvenile unemployment, has demonstrated how successful and how democratic such service projects can be.

For adults, many of these outlets will also be possible; in addition, they can contribute their energies and their skills to various community projects. And part of their spells of service can be devoted to refresher courses designed to improve their professional skill and their outlook as citizens.

Does this appear Utopian? If it does, it is mainly because our competitive society makes it appear so. In a society in which the profit motive has become subsidiary, and which provides economic and social security for all its citizens, workers will no longer fear being thrown out of work by national service schemes, nor will private enterprise be jealous of such projects. In Russia, the "Volunteer Brigades" already did something of the sort, but only to help in emergencies. It remains for the democracies to generalize the system in some form of true national service, and in such a way that the work that gets done is of real value to the community, while at the same time giving the individual a sense of satisfaction and achievement.

But service is only part of the story. Self-expression and self-development are as necessary and as desirable as self-sacrifice, and men and women have as much right to personal enjoyment and a full individual life as the community has to call upon their services. I do not mean to imply that individual expression ·and community service are in separate watertight compartments: some people find the greatest enhancement of their individuality in a shared enterprise designed for the common good, and others, like some types of thinkers and artists, may render their greatest service to the community by developing their individual powers to the utmost. But there is a perfectly real general distinction between the two, and our new order must give play to both.

Perhaps the first thing to remember is that the vast majority of people to-day are simply unaware of the possibilities of fuller living which might be theirs. And this applies to service as much as to individual enjoyment. Before the war, most of us would have pooh-poohed the idea that we could enjoy hard and even dangerous work on behalf of others and the community at large. But, in spite of everything, there are to-day thousands who, though they may sometimes grumble, at heart have enjoyed fighting fires or acting as wardens or serving in canteens. Only recently I heard of a local group of Women's Voluntary Service workers in the lowlands of Scotland whose chief concern was how they might make sure that their work should continue after the war was over.

To an equal extent, this unawareness is true of self-development and enjoyment. Most of us just accept the world into which we are born. We may be acutely conscious that we would like a fuller life than we have got, but what we would like to fill it with consists in general merely of more of the enjoyments which our particular civilization already provides—more leisure to go to cinemas or football matches or dog-races, more opportunity to indulge little private hobbies, more money to cut more of a dash with, more opportunities of doing what the envied richer classes do with their wealth and leisure—smart display, travel cruises, expensive sport, dancing. All these have their merits and their function in life; but there are other possibilities which are simply not thought of by most of us to-day, but which, if they could be realized, would put in the second place much that now has first place in our minds, would provide people with ways of spending their time and energies which many of them would prefer. A well-known sociologist once spoke of the "accursed wantlessness of the common people": most of us do not even know what we lack.

When we look at this question of leisure enjoyment and self-expression in the most general way, we find three striking facts about our present system of things. First, our physical environment, and more particularly that of our big towns and cities, is not designed to make what in brief we may call the good life easier of attainment. Secondly, recreation and cultural activities are not regarded as social services, in which the State should step in on a large scale as it has with education or health or social security. They are, apart from uninfluential and often frustrated "highbrow" groups, preponderantly in the hands of profit-making interests. What with football, racing, the cinema, the theatre, popular literature, and holiday resorts, recreation is to-day one of the most profitable commercial rackets. That being so, standardization is encouraged, and this in turn encourages the spectator mentality: more and more people become passive consumers of amusement, instead of active participants in recreation. Thirdly, our society has not attained social self-consciousness. One half of it does not know how the other half lives; except in times of war, there is little national feeling; and there is a sad absence of group awareness, group pride, or group expression in the cities and towns and rural districts of which the nation is made up. I spoke earlier of the "wantlessness of the people": to know what we might enjoy, as individuals and as a community, and to have the conscious will to get it, is another essential element, now lacking, in social self-consciousness.

Let us try to glimpse some of the promises that the future might hold. The most concrete concerns deliberate planning for recreation and expression. J. B. Priestley once said that modern Britain is an urban civilization without any urban culture. Nearly three-quarters of its people live in towns: yet our towns are so unplanned that they put obstacles in the way of their citizens enjoying not merely the good life, but many of the elementary decencies of existence. The first step is for us to realize that a city need not be a frustrater of life: it can be, among other things, a mechanism for enhancing life, for producing possibilities of living which are not to be realized except through cities. But for that to happen, deliberate and drastic planning is needed. Towns, as much as animals, must have their systems of organs—those for transport and circulation are an obvious example. What we need now are organ-systems for recreation, leisure, culture, community expression. This means smoke-prevention, abundance of open space, easy access to unspoilt nature, beauty in parks and in fine buildings, gymnasia and swimming-baths and recreation-grounds in plenty, central spaces for celebrations and demonstrations, halls for citizens' meetings, concert halls and theatres and cinemas that belong to the city. And the buildings must not be built anyhow or dumped down anywhere; both they and their groupings should mean something important to the people of the place. For the majority of boroughs to-day, the only civic centre is the town hall, which to most people means merely a building that you occasionally have to visit on some tiresome business. But a real city centre would be a place to which people would be coming and going all the time on all kinds of errands of life—with its public halls, its schools (themselves grown into community centres instead of just collections of classrooms), its theatre and cinema, its market, its swimming-baths, its art gallery and its library; and the whole planned as something to be proud of, designed round its central square, and adjoining its park and its tennis courts and recreation grounds.

The Town Hall at Stockholm has been called one of the modern wonders of the world. At any rate, the people of Stockholm are intensely proud of it, and it means a great deal to them. We want this same feeling in our cities, but extended to all the organs and expressions of fuller living.

And do not let us forget beauty. In this England of ours to-day, people have got so used to commercialism that they fight shy of even thinking about beauty. But beauty can play a very concrete part in life. I lived for a time in Oxford; I must confess that the one satisfaction of life in Oxford which I really miss in London was the opportunity it provided of finding beauty on every hand—in the streets, in the College buildings, in the gardens. And it was a very solid satisfaction, which made life easier to live.

But besides the satisfaction of that sort of beauty, there is the satisfaction of art. By art I do not mean merely collections of old masters, or new masters for that matter, essential as they are (one of the deprivations of war-time London is the absence of good pictures—not being able to dash in to the National Gallery or the Tate for half an hour and come out refreshed); I mean living art, including architecture, used as part of the community's way of expressing itself. In Italy in the fourteenth, fifteenth, and early sixteenth centuries, cities vied with each other in their buildings, their sculpture, their pictures, their frescoes. The church of St. Anthony at Padua was built because the Paduans wanted a building to rival St. Mark's at Venice; great masters like Michelangelo and Leonardo were bribed away from one place to another by powerful patrons eager to outshine their rivals.

In America, under the New Deal, numbers of artists were

employed to design frescoes and pictures and mosaics for post-offices and railway stations and the like, so that the United States is the only large modern democracy to have even the beginnings of a public art. In this, as in many other ways, the smaller democracies are in the lead. Sweden and, especially, Mexico, for instance, have a well-developed public art.

Art, if it is good art, is the effective expression of a vital experience. As such, it helps people to discover certain aspects of life that they could not be expected to discover for themselves. And it can also, if it is in harmony with the times, help a community or a nation to express itself and to become more fully conscious of itself. If it is regarded by many people as mere highbrow dilettantism, that is because our commercial-minded individualist society has refused it its true social place. Our New Order must not repeat that mistake.

This links up with the idea of recreation and culture as social services. During the war, a beginning has been made with this, by organizations such as C.E.M.A. and E.N.S.A., which provide concerts, travelling exhibitions of art and architecture, and the like. In the United States, in the early days of the New Deal, a great deal was done along these lines under the W.P.A.—the writers' and artists' and theatre projects. The theatre project indeed began to create new types of popular drama like the Living Newspaper, which undoubtedly stimulated social self-consciousness. But unfortunately (as it seems to many of us) all these activities have now been abolished.

What the future may bring forth we cannot know. But we do know that human beings can attain some of their richer satisfactions through art and music, whether in creating, performing, or enjoying them; and that there is no reason why the rich patrons of earlier centuries should not be replaced by the State, by city governments, by big corporations. There is no reason why, within a generation, the life of Britain should not be vivified by art and satisfying

ritual as the life of Western European nations was vivified
in the late Middle Ages and the early Renaissance.

Finally, besides the satisfaction of service and of expression, there is that of creation. I have said a word about the
professional artist, whose creativeness is too often frustrated
and inhibited under our present system. But exhibitions of
children's art, such as those organized in recent years by the
L.C.C., demonstrate what reservoirs of talent and what
opportunities for self-expression are hidden in the ordinary
child; while the few tentative experiments that have been
made show that a great many adults, if given the opportunity,
could find satisfaction (like Mr. Churchill) in painting,
just for the sake of finding an outlet for the creative impulse,
without bothering about exhibiting their work.

However, the creative spirit can find outlets in innumerable other ways than in art. Private hobbies are often, in our
present type of society, the only outlet for creative self-
expression. If a man could indulge his hobby by contributing
to some communal project, he would find a double satisfaction. Work, too, can become more satisfying if it satisfies
the creative impulse and if those who work feel that they are
creating something for themselves and for the community at
large, not merely for their employers or for the State. In
the most general terms, the more the private profit motive
is socialized and made to take a back seat in relation to the
common good, and the more the community becomes conscious of itself as a community, the more satisfaction will
quite ordinary people find in quite ordinary work. They will
find satisfaction in proportion as they feel that they are
helping to build something which belongs to them in common with all the rest of their particular group. That spirit
is manifest in every kind of professional pride; it contributed
a great deal to the success that Soviet Russia has achieved
(and there have been many successes as well as some
failures); it was at work in Nazi Germany. It could be
operative in democracies like Britain or the United States.
Perhaps we need a four-year plan for Britain, as the Prime
Minister has promised us, and one with clearly defined

social objectives. But there is no doubt that the creative spirit could and should be harnessed in any New Order that we envisage.

These are a few glimpses, as my own groping vision sees them, of what the New Order of social man might look like after the old concept of economic man has gone into the discard. Many people, I am sure, will say that such a type of society is contrary to human nature. On that point, however, I am equally sure, speaking as a biologist, that they are wrong. For one thing, the majority of human beings always begin by regarding any large change as contrary to nature, human or otherwise. Then, if it is said that personal self-interest and the economic profit motive are the only incentives that will get things done, that is contrary to experience. Not only Hitler's success in inspiring fanatical enthusiasm in a powerful minority of Germans, but our own reaction in Britain since Mr. Churchill told us that he had nothing to offer but blood and toil, tears and sweat, demonstrates the strength of incentives like sacrifice and devotion. To speak from my professional knowledge, the life of the great majority of scientists is a demonstration that men and women of more than average qualities are willing to spend their lives without hope of more than a very moderate income, because their work is interesting and creative and they feel that it is useful. The struggling artist is a demonstration of the strength of the urge to self-expression; and Russia's and Germany's five- and four-year plans are proof of the power of large-scale social constructiveness.

It has been England's boast that since the Norman conquest she has evolved by creative compromise where other nations have been subject to violent revolutions. We are now faced with perhaps the severest test in our history. Can we effect the drastic transformation from the age of economic man to the age of social man, from individualist *laisser-faire* to a highly organized society, by evolutionary means, without violence or civil war? And can we effect it in such a way as not only to remain democratic but to raise democracy to new and heightened expression?

No one can tell. There are powerful forces working against any such change. But there are also reservoirs of sanity and idealism that can be mobilized for it. Democracy will have to struggle hard to survive and to transform itself; it will have to struggle against enemies within as well as enemies without. But at the moment it is still very much alive. There are still plenty of grounds for hope, and plenty of opportunities for work in the service of that hope.

THE WAR: TWO JOBS, NOT ONE

ONCE, years ago, when I was on a lecture tour across the United States, I found myself in Texas when Ma Ferguson was campaigning for Governor of that great state. One of the things I remember about that campaign is a huge poster of Ma Ferguson, pictured as a very motherly sort of homebody, with her husband behind, looking over her shoulder; and underneath, after exhortations to vote for the lady, the slogan, "Two Governors for the Price of One."

To-day we have the possibility—indeed, the necessity—of doing two jobs—two enormous world-jobs—at the price of one. So far, most of us have only bothered about one of the jobs—getting on with the war. But over the shoulder of the war something else is looming up—something even bigger than the war.

That something is no less than a world transformation. And by a world transformation I mean a process of drastic change, when history is being made much more quickly than usual, and the whole framework of the ideas and institutions by which and in which we live is being entirely reshaped into a quite new form.

As a man builds himself a house, so humanity builds itself a civilization to live in. For centuries humanity goes on inhabiting the same house. A window is put in here, a new room thrown out there, the furniture and the interior decoration are changed; but in spite of all the alterations, it is still the same house. Then, one fine day, humanity pulls the old house down and builds a new one, in a different style, with different plans, new types of construction, and new conveniences. Perhaps some of the old materials are used in the new structure, some of the old furniture and pictures are kept to decorate the new rooms; but it is a new house, a new kind of a house, a new civilization for men to inhabit. A world transformation has taken place.

During the course of history, humanity has been through a number of these drastic transformations. One of the most familiar to us is the period of the Renaissance and Reformation, while another is that of the Industrial Revolution. During the Renaissance and the Reformation the Middle Ages were transformed into a more modern kind of world, where individual freedom of enterprise in exploration and business and politics, and individual freedom of judgment and inquiry in religion and philosophy and science, became substituted for the rigid framework of feudalism and the equally rigid framework of orthodox religious philosophy. During the Industrial Revolution (with which the American and French and Latin-American revolutions are linked) the pre-scientific world gave place to a world where individual enterprise found new frontiers opened to it by technology, where competitive economic enterprise was freed from innumerable restrictions, nationalism became the main driving force in world politics, and natural science at last began to play an important part in shaping the background of thought.

It is this world, brought into being by the Industrial Revolution, which is now destined to disappear and be remodelled in the new transformation through which we ourselves are living to-day.

Do you doubt it? It is perfectly possible to do so, possible to live in the middle of a world transformation and not realize the fact of its existence. A world transformation is so enormous in scale and, however rapid in terms of ordinary history, so slow in terms of human life. It is easy to concentrate on single symptoms—the war, or the depression, or the unrest in India, or the New Deal—rather than on the giant process as a whole. But it is the whole which counts. Unless we first recognize the existence of the world transformation, then do our best to understand it, and, finally, embark on it of set purpose in order to make it happen the way we want, we shall never release all the forces of democracy. Too many of those forces are still latent: that is why Hitler was able to sneer at us as sluggish and decadent "pluto-democracies." But if we can mobilize their full potential, Democracy could become more dynamic than Fascism or Communism or any other ism or ideology.

These are fine words: let us get back to hard facts. What is this transformation in which we are caught up; and where is it taking us? Is it something wholly beyond our control, like an earthquake, or can we jump into the saddle and guide it toward a desired destination? Let us look at recent history and see what are the trends of change and what they have in common.

In the first place, this transformation, like all other world transformations in the past, is, in some form or other, quite inescapable: certain general tendencies will work themselves out to their furthest conclusions whatever we say or do, whether we like them or whether we dislike them. They will do so because the transformation is the result of huge economic and social forces which are entirely beyond our control. The nineteenth-century system, which worked excellently in one set of conditions, itself produced new conditions in which it worked badly: its very success in the long run defeated itself. Its two chief characteristics were *laisser-faire* economics and nationalism. The *laisser-faire* system of freely competing private enterprise created a new level of prosperity. But, with its eyes fixed on profits, it neglected conservation and amenities: the result was deforestation, soil erosion, the dust bowl, the ugliest cities in history. With its belief that individual initiative, working under the laws of supply and demand, would automatically produce the most rapid progress possible, it neglected social organization and planning: the result was a series of violent trade cycles, culminating in the great depression, the conversion of customer countries into competitors, the growth of big business, monopolies, and cartels by the competitive squeezing out of the small firm, the increase of unemployment with consequent insecurity and sense of frustration.

In world politics, nationalism led to an increase of

patriotic cohesion and of military and naval efficiency, and
to a rapid exploitation of the resources of backward countries,
coupled with a sense of a colonial mission. In America, the
open frontier took the place of the undeveloped tropics,
and the expansion of the United States of America occurred
within its own boundaries: "Go West, young man," took
the place of the "White Man's Burden," and pioneering of
imperialism. But gradually the world shrank in effective
size, the frontier closed, the undeveloped areas were all
taken over. Nationalist competition, which had begun as
military rivalry, ended in unhealthy and perpetual friction.
Sovereign independence became transformed into autarky
and self-sufficiency.

Thus to economic insecurity and the dread of unemployment were added political insecurity and the dread of war.
In the background, a sense of frustration and aimlessness had
begun to take the place of hope and purpose. The system,
once solid, had become unstable. *Laisser-faire* and nationalism worked well in an expanding world of open frontiers.
They themselves helped to close the frontiers and bring
expansion to an end: until in the closed, tightly knit world
of the twentieth century there is no longer room for the
particular kind of freedom of *laisser-faire*, and the sovereign
independence of nations has become a dangerous fiction.
Some other system is bound to be born, because the old
system will no longer work.

In the United States, with its advanced industrialization
and its isolated position, and its huge undeveloped resources,
it took longer for the old system to begin breaking up than
in any other important country, just as the United States
was the last of the great Powers to be drawn into the war.
But the same inexorable processes are at work here as
elsewhere.

If we look back at the last quarter of a century, we find
country after country adopting new methods to compensate
for the break-down of the old. Sometimes the old system is
rejected entire, and a wholly new one deliberately set up.
When that happens, the transformation becomes a true

revolution. Since 1917 there have been revolutions in Russia, in Italy, in Turkey, in China, in Germany, in Spain, in Portugal, in a pale sort of way in Vichy France, and in other countries. In all these cases the revolution has been wholly or mainly totalitarian, though in Spain, Portugal, and Russia it began by being democratic; in China its totalitarianism has been a matter of military necessity and political expediency, and it contains a good deal of actual and a great deal of potential democracy.

However, countries can suffer radical transformation without passing through a revolution. Japan, for instance, has always been totalitarian. In recent times it has transformed itself from tribal and feudal totalitarianism to a modern technological totalitarianism. It anticipated Hitler in calling for the complete subordination of the individual to the State, and in ideas of a "new order." To-day, Japan is a planned ultra-patriotic totalitarian state, though there it is not a dictator who wields power, but a group of army leaders and politicians.

Finally, you can have a transformation which is non-revolutionary and also democratic. So far, this particular kind of transformation has nowhere been completed; but it has gone quite a way in a number of countries.

In Sweden and other Scandinavian nations it revealed itself in the form of sweeping measures of social security and welfare—health and unemployment insurance, old age and widows' pensions, the equalizing of educational opportunity, subsidized housing and vitamin-rich food for the under-privileged, minimum wage laws, a constructive population policy, and so on.

The British Dominions, most notably perhaps New Zealand, moved independently along a closely parallel course. The same trends, though in many ways not so sweeping, were followed by Britain between the two wars, and have become accentuated during the present war. In the United States the New Deal represented a partial but very sudden instalment of the transformation.

Internationally, things were happening too. The League

of Nations, the first attempt at world-wide international organization, came into being. Even when it began to fail and finally collapsed as a political institution, various of its branches, like the International Labour Office and the Health section, continued doing useful work. What is more, the failure of the League merely served to underline the urgent need for *some* international political organization. Hitler's vision of this is the "new order," through which he has already gone a long way toward making Europe a unit. Japan's vision is the East Asia Co-Prosperity Sphere. The United Nations have their vision of such an organization, though it is as yet much vaguer. On the other hand, they have already undertaken various concrete pieces of international organization during the war which could readily continue in modified form after it is over—Lend-Lease, the leasing and sharing of strategic bases, unified committees for supply and other functions, the Middle East Supply Council, the Anglo-American Caribbean Commission, and now the Triple-Allied Advisory Council for Italy, and, perhaps most important of all, the European Advisory Commission. The most fundamental change, however, is that the world has not only become a unit but that it has recognized the fact that it has become a unit. National isolation, including isolationism, has become more and more impossible and unrealistic.

Another international aspect of the transformation has been the greater concern over backward areas and peoples. Sometimes this has revealed itself merely in a desire to exploit material resources—oil in Mexico or Persia, copper in Central Africa, tin in Malaya, and so forth. Sometimes it is focused on political advance, as with the United States' guidance of the Filipinos along the road to independence, sometimes on social and economic welfare, as with the British and the Anglo-American commissions now in the West Indies. Sometimes it is thinking of all-round development, as in the increased sums of money made available during the war by Britain for her colonies, and their utilization for social as well as material development. Sometimes it is concerned with backward regions inside the nation, as with the Depressed Areas in Britain, or the Tennessee Valley Authority in the United States. Sometimes action has been forced by the demand of the dependent peoples, as recently in India. Sometimes even, as in Europe since the spring of 1940, the more powerful nation has forcibly driven others into backwardness, the better to be able to exploit their resources. At the opposite extreme, there was the establishment of the Mandate system, which, for all its unreality in certain respects, did establish the principle that some backward areas at least were not possessions but were the responsibility of the world at large, not merely of some single Power.

At first sight, this jumble of events and tendencies may seem to reveal no common characteristics. Sudden revolution and slow evolution as processes; democracy and dictatorship as methods; exploitation and emancipation for backward peoples; social welfare and military aggression as national aim—what elements can these have in common? However, when we look more closely, we find that all over the world the transformation pursues certain broad trends which are everywhere similar in direction, while the differences are in their form. There is a trend away from *laisser-faire* toward planning; there is a tendency for the Government to take a more positive hand in an increasing number of the activities of life; there is a trend to put purely economic motives and aims into the second place, in favour of non-economic motives and aims; there is an increasing concern with the material and human resources of backward regions; and there is a growing realization of the impossibility of national isolation and of the necessity for some strong and thorough-going international organization.

Those are the common elements in the transformation, and they seem to be inescapable tendencies of the times, as inevitable as were the trends, a century and a half ago, toward mechanized private enterprise and the other main tendencies of the Industrial Revolution. In some form or another they will accomplish themselves. But the form

itself is not inescapable: there are alternatives. For one
thing, the transformation may be got through faster or
slower, with more friction or with less. That depends on
whether we co-operate with the inevitable tendencies or
whether we resist them. When Margaret Fuller was
reported as saying, "I accept the Universe," Carlyle remarked, "Gad, she'd better!" The general trends of a world
transformation are part of the facts of the universe, and it
will certainly be better if as many of us as possible accept
them and deliberately try to help the transformation on its
way.

The people who talk, or have talked, about "the Wave of
the Future" have seen this. But they have seen it crooked;
they have not perceived the second alternative, the second
cross-roads in the route which the transformation may take.
And this second alternative is more important than the first.
The first was a choice of quantity—whether the transformation should go faster or slower. The second is a choice as to
quality. Shall it be peaceful, co-operative, democratic, or shall
it be militarist, totalitarian, brutal?

The believers in the Wave of the Future said, correctly
enough, that a transformation had taken place in Nazi
Germany, and that Germany had thereby become more
efficient, more unified, more disciplined, more willing to
make sacrifices, more proudly conscious of itself and its
destiny; it no longer suffered from the hesitations and cross-
purposes of the democracies, their lack of aim, their lack of
a sense of satisfying purpose in life. They, therefore, concluded not merely that the democracies also ought deliberately to undertake their own transformation, but that this
should follow the German model.

The first part of their conclusion was correct, the second
was not. They were right in saying that the democracies
had to go through with this process of transforming the
framework of their existence, and that they ought to undertake the business deliberately, with a definite purpose in
view. Failure to do this may spell disaster through inefficiency and unpreparedness. Hitler and the Nazis believed

that Britain had drifted into this position, and would fall to them like an over-ripe plum after the collapse of France. In fact, it nearly did so: but the English Channel, the R.A.F., Mr. Churchill, and the reserves of character and determination in the people at large, just saved it.

Failure to face the need for the transformation and for getting on with it purposefully may even cause a country to go to pieces in an emergency. If those who happen not to like a world transformation obstinately resist it, and if the rest of the nation are divided in their ideas of how the transformation should be made, so that the transforming forces are divided and begin pulling in different directions, then the whole framework of society may be so weakened that it collapses under strain. That was what happened in France.

So far, then, the believers in the Wave of the Future were right. But they were wrong in concluding that there was only one kind of Wave of the Future, namely, the totalitarian Fascist model, exemplified most fully in Nazi Germany. There is also a democratic model. Or, rather, a democratic model is possible. Their mistake was in a way pardonable, for already some time before the war Germany and various other totalitarian countries had got through their transformation fairly completely, while nowhere had a transformation of democratic type gone more than part way toward completion, and nowhere had it been deliberately undertaken.

One of the reasons that no complete model of a democratic transformation as yet exists is the slowness of democracies; they take more time than totalitarian states to make up their minds. Perhaps that is inevitable, perhaps not: at any rate, it is true of democracies in their present form. However, another reason is that it is more difficult to get through this particular transformation in a democratic way than in a totalitarian way. Totalitarianism, in fact, provides a political short-cut toward stability and unity. Whether it ever actually gets there is another matter—whether its unity is ever wholly real, its stability ever permanent. But for the time being it certainly can achieve a good deal of unity and stability very quickly. A totalitarian regime is able to do this because it is able to suppress contrary opinions and impose its own ideas, to distort justice and science and religion to further its own ends, to drive its opponents into exile or shut them up in concentration camps, to take far-reaching decisions immediately, to impose plans irrespective of the wishes of the people —in a word, because it is totalitarian, and, being totalitarian, can and does use force to do what it likes.

The problem before a democracy is much harder. It may realize that more planning and more government control are inevitable, that the automatic operation of economic motives is not enough to produce a satisfying life, that greater unification and a more conscious sense of unity are necessary, that international organization is urgently required. But how is democracy to achieve this and yet stay democratic? Planning, for instance—there are plenty of people in the United States who quite genuinely believe that planning is the thin end of the totalitarian wedge, that any government control means starting down a slope that leads inevitably to 100 per cent. regimentation. The free play of economic motives —this certainly was the American way which produced such quick results in the past: why shouldn't it continue to do so in the future? Anyhow, how are you going to get people to put some other motive in the first place without undemocratic compulsion? Then there is the feeling of unity. How is it possible to achieve this without substituting propaganda for freedom of the Press and untrammelled expression of opinion, without forcibly muzzling those with minority views? And, finally, how can you make nations join an international organization without doing violence to the democratic principles of national freedom and self-determination? Britain and the United States, together, if they wanted to, might well be strong enough to make most of the rest of the world join an organization dominated by them, but that would hardly be democratic.

Once more, the answer is that it is difficult, but can be done. Planning can be democratic, as has been best demonstrated in the United States themselves. The Tennessee

Valley Authority, for instance, in everything except its direct executive job of building dams and power plants, does not forcibly impose its plans on the regions. It improves agriculture and checks erosion by persuasion—it persuades farmers to volunteer to use improved fertilizers and improved methods on their farms, until the results persuade other farmers to do the same. It does not even distribute the electricity it generates; it persuades towns and rural areas to create their own distribution organizations. It does not force new methods on people; but it has designed a number of agricultural and electric appliances suitable for small farmers and rural consumers, which it then makes available (via licence through private firms) at low cost. It does not insist on town-planning schemes, but it puts its research facilities and its expert advisers at the disposal of any town that wants to plan itself. It does not impose a plan forcibly from above; it does not even say, "Here is a good plan—take it or leave it." It helps local communities to plan for themselves and it tries to get a general sense of participation on the part of the people of the region through the voluntary collaboration of the educational authorities and in other ways. Far from crushing private enterprise, planning here has aided it. Agriculture is still carried on by individual farmers, but they are more prosperous; a number of new factories have been started, attracted by cheap power; and quite new activities, like water transportation and boatbuilding and boat-hiring for pleasure, have been thrown open to private enterprise.

In the North-west, in the huge area to be served by the Bonneville and Grand Coulee dams on the Columbia River, planning is even more radically democratic. The general outline of the plan is being threshed out on the spot, partly by an official committee, partly by a purely private and voluntary organization, the North-west Regional Commission, which represents local communities and private interests.

In general, within the framework of a plan, plenty of room

THE WAR: TWO JOBS, NOT ONE

can be left for individual initiative, and certain sectors of life can deliberately be left unplanned.

As regards motive, war is the clearest demonstration of how economic incentives can be made to take second place. But it would be equally possible to make patriotism the chief motive in peace-time, a patriotism which takes pride in the achievements of the whole nation. A people can be proud of having the lowest infant mortality in the world, or of increasing the number of those with a college education, of abolishing malnutrition and slums, of possessing beautiful cities and fine orchestras. In Russia there is immense pride in new scientific discoveries, or in the success of a difficult expedition, and as much interest in them as the English-speaking peoples evince in sport. Anyhow, sport is another non-economic outlet. Besides, there are the powerful motives of service and sacrifice, of self-development and adventure. If outlets can be organized for these, we can be sure that full advantage will be taken of them by human nature.

Unity is perhaps a harder problem: but it, too, is not impossible of democratic solution. Unity may be achieved through uniformity; but it does not have to be, and unity in and through diversity is fuller and richer. One aid to unity is to have a truly national culture—music, films, writing, radio, art, architecture—which reflects all the diverse facets of national life and makes a people conscious of itself and its corporate existence, its destiny and its ideals. Ancient Athens had such a culture. So did the Renaissance, but it was largely restricted to the privileged classes. No large modern nation has yet developed one which is shared by all sections of the people. In the democracies culture is still sectional, and what there is of it often reflects life in a distorted way, as with films in the United States. But there is no reason why a general culture of this sort should not exist. Russia has deliberately set out to create one, and has gone a considerable way toward doing so. War-time film-making, especially perhaps in Canada, is making the movie a comprehensive and faithful mirror for the war-time life and purpose of peoples. Cultural unity which is both many-sided and democratic is at any rate possible.

A high level of universal education can also make both for unification and for the sense of unity; so can the provision of large-scale organizations for service—youth service, military service (as in Switzerland), civilian service, workers' voluntary service, and so on. Finally, the putting of non-economic motives in first place, above economic motives, can help to produce unity. Purely economic motives on the whole tend to rivalry and disunity; so do certain non-economic motives such as the craving for power for its own sake. But patriotic motives, whether the patriotism of war or the patriotism of peace, make for collective pride and unified purpose. And motives that transcend even the nation, as can be the case with science, with religion, with art, with the relief of suffering, may equally make for unity and co-operation.

Finally, there is the difficulty of making international organization democratic. But is this really so great? The United States itself came into existence by organizing originally independent sovereign units into a greater whole. England and Scotland, once separate and often hostile, are now united to form Britain, and that too is a democratic co-operative union. During this war, Germany has had to force Hungary, Rumania, Finland, and Italy into joint military action; but the joint supply and military measures of the United Nations, including drastic restrictions of national sovereignty, like the leasing and pooling of bases, are all on a voluntary, co-operative basis, and so are the arrangements, already well advanced, for bringing food and medical relief into the enemy-occupied countries as soon as the war is won.

.   .   .   .   .

The need for getting on with the transformation quickly and of set purpose is also of importance for the war itself. It is a fact of observation that those nations which have got through the transformation more completely have, in general, shown greater military efficiency. In the language of the statistician, the two facts show a marked positive correlation, and the degree of transformation undoubtedly helps to produce the military efficiency. It is not merely that the totalitarian nations have been preparing longer for war: it is that the totalitarian nations are also the more completely transformed. Germany shows the most radical transformation of any nation: and in Germany you find the most thorough planning; the economic profit motive is there completely subordinated to the motive of war and national aggrandisement; the nation is formidably united behind its own ideal of an "Aryan" Master-Race, and against the bogy scape-goat enemies of the Jews, Bolshevism, and "pluto-democracy"; and as soon as it got the chance, it has set about organizing an international "new order" in the most drastic way.

Russia is also very thoroughly transformed, and much more efficient militarily than almost anyone expected. The efficiency is not merely in production or in tactics; it springs also from the unity which the transformation has helped to bring about in the people.

The transformation effected by Fascism in Italy was never so thoroughgoing as that produced by Nazism in Germany; and in correlation with this (though doubtless with other factors too) Italy's military efficiency has not been so high. In France the transformation itself and the methods of achieving it were matters of acute controversy, so that unity was decreased and purposeful planning made more difficult; and the result, in spite of high technical skill and proud traditions, was military inefficiency and political collapse.

In the democratic countries, the changes which have been found necessary, some by bitter experience, to increase military efficiency, are all changes toward more central planning and control, toward the subordination of the profit motive and all ideas of "business as usual" to the non-economic motive of success in war, toward greater unity, and toward more thoroughgoing international arrangements—four main trends of the world transformation.

Many details will have to be altered later to adapt the new machinery from the ends of war to those of peace. But without doubt much of the change has undoubtedly come to stay. The transformation is inescapable, and in the world after the war more planning, more unity, and more international organization will still be necessary.

But the planning and the unity and the international organization must be of the right kind. Thus the next step must be to make sure that our transformation, when we go through with it, is a democratic one.

Are there any general rules for us to go on when we are constructing the new framework of the world's life, to make sure we are not taking the easy short-cuts that lead to totalitarianism? Are there any principles of democracy which will apply as much in the world that is being born as they did in the age that is coming to an end? It is certainly not enough to say that democracy is freedom of individual enterprise, or representative government with free elections. The former applied only to democracy in a particular stage of civilization, when *laisser-faire* economics was the best way of achieving advance. The latter is only one part of the machinery of only one aspect of democracy—political democracy. We have got to find more general principles, and we have got to translate our old principles into new terms that will apply in new conditions.

There seems to be only one universal principle of democracy, applicable in any and every phase of history. It is that human individuals are the democratic measuring-rod. The satisfaction of the needs of individual human beings is one side of the picture; and the other is their free and active participation in the life of the society to which they belong. Satisfaction of needs means a basic platform of health and welfare, security and freedom for all, together with equal opportunity for further individual development, through education, recreation, adventure, service, and self-expression. Participation means that the individual feels himself to be a part of a greater whole, that he co-operates in the general affairs of this community and nation, and that he is given the opportunity of sharing in as many activities of society as possible. Everywhere the rights and the duties of individuals are what counts.

In addition, there are certain principles that will be applicable in the new phase in which we are entering. The chief characteristic of that new stage is that the world, though still consisting of distant nations, has become a unit, so that no country can escape being influenced by what is happening in other parts of the world, and the nations are becoming much less distinct and their affairs much more closely entangled with those of other nations. The consequence of this is the inescapable trend we have already mentioned, toward some form of international organization for both economic and political security, which will help prosperity and prevent war.

What is the democratic way of building up such an organization? The first essential is that it should be based on freedom and equality of opportunity—free and equal co-operation, instead of domination based on inequality of force. The pooling of strategic bases for common use is an example of equal co-operation in the military sphere. In the economic sphere, an example is the joint control of certain key raw materials to prevent booms and depressions and to increase consumption. The second essential is that the authority which has to take decisions on international matters should, as far as possible, represent peoples and not national governments. This is another way of saying that individual participation is needed in the international as well as the national sphere. The decision of the Thirteen States to form the United States was taken by their peoples, not by their governments. Perhaps the participation of peoples in the new World Order will at the outset be confined to making the decision to unite for certain purposes. Later on, more and more power must be given to individual citizens, until eventually some sort of elected federal government comes into being.

Free and equal co-operation applies to peoples which are sufficiently advanced to stand on their own feet as distinct nations. But what about those others, forming between a quarter and a third of the world's population, which are still so backward that they must be administered as dependent colonies, or those which are nominally independent but still require a certain amount of help or tutelage or guidance? The answer is, I think, quite clear. In the new unit world, the inescapable trend is, as already set forth, for greater attention to be paid to the development of their human and material resources. If they cannot be treated as actual equals, the democratic way of realizing that trend is to treat them as potential equals. That means helping their peoples to achieve self-government as quickly as possible, and developing their material resources not by one-sided exploitation but as part of a co-operative scheme.

If we want to be still clearer as to our guiding principles as believers in democracy, we can study the way totalitarianism works and adopt methods as far removed as possible from those which it employs. Looked at in this way, democracy means the absence of secret police and concentration camps, of irresponsible dictatorships or oligarchies, of muzzled opinion, of brute force as the mainstay of government, of inequality of opportunity, of one-sided domination and one-sided exploitation.

.   .   .   .   .

There remains one final question. How are we to enter upon the transformation consciously, formally, and with the greatest possible energy? The answer is clear—by proclaiming peace aims which include the achieving of the transformation. Once more, this can be done in a totalitarian way or in a democratic way. Hitler has proclaimed his aims. They are quite comprehensive and fairly detailed. They include the dominance of the so-called Aryan race and of the Germanic nation; the National-Socialist transformation of Germany; the destruction of what he is pleased to call "pluto-democracy" and of Bolshevism; the servitude of the Jews; and an elaborate international organization in the form of a "new order" in which Germany controls and exploits as many other countries as possible.

Hitler's aim of a "new order" in Europe was anticipated by many years by the Japanese "new order"—now re-christened Co-Prosperity Sphere—in East Asia. The long-declared aim of this is to establish complete Japanese supremacy in the Far East, with Japan in a privileged economic and military position. "Asia for the Asiatics" is a further aim, with the destruction of all trade of "white imperialism" in the region.

Both the German and the Japanese aims are represented as the crusade of a chosen race, for which no sacrifices are too great; and as such they undoubtedly make a powerful emotional appeal to people at large.

These are the war and peace aims of our totalitarian enemies. They are comprehensive, and boldy envisage the achieving of the world transformation, not as a hostile process to be resisted, not as a necessity to be tolerated, but as an opportunity to be seized, a mission to be embarked upon. Just because this is so, they have enlisted much of the emotional forces of their peoples: the mission is embarked upon with fervour, the opportunity treated as one for dedication, effort, and sacrifice in a cause transcending self.

There is no reason why the United Nations should not do the same—the same, only different, because in a democratic way; the same, only more potent, because the democratic ideal is in the long run more powerful in its appeal. The Nazi ideal of a united Europe had a strong appeal to the peoples of the Continent; but that appeal is being destroyed by bitter experience of the totalitarian methods employed. The Nazi ideal of a chosen Nordic race with a noble mission makes a strong appeal to Germans; but that appeal too is being undermined as the troops in occupied countries find they are regarded not as liberators or friends, but as hated oppressors.

It would be possible for us to declare a set of peace aims which would release the latest dynamism of democracy and reveal it as the most potent political and social force in existence; which would unite all those who believe in freedom, decency, and justice; and which would satisfy the aspirations of the world's underfed and underprivileged millions for a fuller life. But this will not happen unless we first become aware of the world transformation, learn to understand it, and treat it as an opportunity to be embraced by democracy.

The war is two jobs in one, and the more obvious job of production and military action is in the long run no more important than this second one of riding the real Wave of the Future by achieving the world transformation in a wholeheartedly democratic way.

PHILOSOPHY IN A WORLD AT WAR

[Note.—When I was in the U.S.A. early in 1942, *Fortune*
magazine was running a series with the above title. After
reading the articles by W. E. Hocking, Professor of Philosophy at Harvard, W. L. Sperry, Dean of the Harvard Divin-
ity School, W. P. Montague, Professor of Philosophy at
Columbia, and Jacques Maritain, the well-known French
writer and scholar, I asked if I might state the biologist's
position; and this essay is the result.]

WHAT has Philosophy to do with War, the one so
abstract and theoretical, the other so terribly concrete
and practical? In point of fact, the two have a great deal to
do with each other. Philosophy in the broad sense is an
attitude to the universe, a *Weltanschauung*, an appraisal
of values in their relation to brute material facts. Its essence,
in Professor Montague's words, is not proof but vision: it
is concerned with what Professor Hocking has called the
continued revision of goals. And war must be about something, must have a goal. No nation ever went to war without
some belief in the value of the war's goal. Even when the
mainspring of a war is merely economic advantage or
conquest, some justification has to be invented—the right-
ness of your cause, or defence against aggression, or the
superiority of your race, or the sacred duty to spread your
religion; and the justification, even if hypocritical in its
origin, will have its effect on the thoughts and actions of
those who fight the war. Even then, and still more in those
numerous cases when moral aims genuinely exist and do not
have to be invented, war is deeply entangled with philosophy.

To-day all the protagonists have a philosophy of the war
they are waging—we in saying that we fight for freedom; the
Germans in saying that they fight for the triumph of the
highest human race; the Russians in saying that they fight
for their fatherland and to rid the world of the evil thing

they call Hitlerism. Such philosophies are all incomplete;
some of them, like the Germans' claim to be a superrace, are
demonstrably erroneous.

The business of Philosophy with a capital P is to provide
us with the completest and truest philosophy possible. Once
we have a philosophy, it can be applied to the immediate
needs of the war, just as pure scientific knowledge can be
applied to satisfy immediate material needs. One of its main
applications lies in its helping us to achieve a stronger morale
and to formulate peace aims. The truer our philosophy, the
more complete, and the more efficiently it is applied to the
circumstances of the war (which of course implies a comprehension of the intricate human, economic, and political
background), the more it will help us to formulate peace
aims which will be not merely satisfying, but themselves an
efficient weapon of war. But conversely, if our philosophy
is false or partial, its application will give us incomplete or
unsatisfactory peace aims, which will have a correspondingly
lower efficiency as psychological weapons.

The Western world to-day is caught in an apparent
dilemma between two conflicting modes of thought. The one
thinks in terms of absolutes—the absoluteness of truth,
beauty, justice, goodness, themselves all deriving from an
Absolute of absolutes, which is God. The natural world is
complemented by the supernatural, the body by the soul,
the temporal by the eternal. This view gives an essentially
static world-picture; the flux of events is merely change,
in which the only progress is a spiritual one, toward the
perfection of eternal values. Empiricism and the experimental method are alien to it; the absolute of Revelation and
the absolute of pure Reason will between them answer all
the questions that can be answered. Man's place in the
universe is the place of an eternal soul, created by God, and
working out its destiny in terms of eternal values.

The other is the scientific method. It subjects the conclusions of reason to the arbitrament of hard fact to build
an increasing body of tested knowledge. It refuses to ask
questions that cannot be answered, and rejects such answers

as cannot be provided except by Revelation. It discovers the relatedness of all things in the universe—of the motion of the moon to the influence of earth and sun, of the nature of the organism to its environment, of human civilization to the conditions under which it is made. It introduces history into everything. Stars and scenery have their history, alike with plant species or human institutions, and nothing is intelligible without some knowledge of its past. As Whitehead has said, each event is the reflection or effect of every other event, past as well as present. It rejects dualism. The supernatural is in part the region of the natural that has not yet been understood, in part an invention of human fantasy, in part the unknowable. Body and soul are not separate entities, but two aspects of one organization, and Man is that portion of the universal world-stuff that has evolved until it is capable of rational and purposeful values. His place in the universe is to continue that evolution and to realize those values.

These two ways of approaching and thinking about the universe are irreconcilable—as irreconcilable as is magic with scientific agriculture, witch-doctoring with preventive medicine, or number-mysticism with higher mathematics. Because our thinking still contains elements from both, it and we are confused.

This is not the view of the previous contributors to this series. In different ways they have maintained that the two systems of thought are not mutually exclusive but complementary. Though they all admit that the scientific or relativist approach is adequate and indeed essential so far as it goes, they agree in asserting that it cannot go all the way—that it is necessarily partial and needs to be supplemented by some elements derived from the alternative way of thinking. Professor Sperry says that we must supplement science with moral universals. Professor Maritain frankly finds the only chance of regeneration in a philosophy based on Christian theology. Professor Montague, more vaguely, postulates a tendency toward ideal good operating in nature—an omnipresent but not omnipotent Holy Spirit strongly reminiscent of Matthew Arnold's "something, not ourselves, which makes for righteousness." Professor Montague calls this a god, without the capital letter. Professor Hocking is more definite: for him the truth of science needs to be supplemented by another truth: that the world "has its own unity in a living purpose: it is the truth of the existence of God."

To me, this mixing of two totally different kinds of thinking can only lead to confusion. When men assert that the scientific approach is incomplete, it is because they have not been willing to follow it to its final conclusion, or because they are mistaking an early stage in its growth for full development.

Science inevitably began by trying its hand on the simpler phenomena of nature. Its first triumphs were in mechanics, including the spectacular celestial mechanics of Newton. It next proceeded to simple physics, like the gas laws or the decomposition of white light. Chemistry, even elementary chemistry, did not take real shape till a century later. The life sciences developed later than those of lifeless matter, for the sufficing reason that they deal with more complex phenomena. Physiology had to wait on physics and chemistry before it could become scientific. Evolution, the central fact of biology, was not established until modern science had been in existence for over two hundred years; the mysteries of heredity did not become clear until well on in the present century. In the same way the science of mind developed later than biological science. What Newton was for mechanics and physics, and Darwin for biology, Freud was for psychology—the originator of a new and illuminating way of thinking about the subject-matter of his science.

It is of some significance that none of the previous writers in this series have even mentioned Freud or taken the finding of modern psychology into consideration at all—not excluding Professor Montague, though he essays a psychological analysis of the development of conscience in the growing child.

This is one of the reasons for their claim that the scientific approach is insufficient. Of course it is insufficient if you leave out the latest stage of its development. You might just as well leave out physiology and evolution and then claim that the scientific approach as represented by classical physics and chemistry was insufficient. No, the only cure for the insufficiency of science is more science. The scientific approach, empirical and where possible experimental, preferring the relative to the absolute, and rejecting the deductions of pure reason except when based upon the inductions of raw fact, cannot be rejected as insufficient until it has been completely tried out on the analysis of human mind and human affairs as well as on that of non-living matter. In these less complex fields its application has already revolutionized our way of thinking about the universe (not to mention producing the most spectacular practical results): there is no reason why it should not continue to do so as it consolidates its hold on the new areas it is now invading. Let us not forget that scientific method is extremely young: what are three centuries compared to the few millennia of civilization, the million years of man, or the thousand million years of evolving life?

Scientific method to-day has reached about as far in its understanding of human mind as it had in the understanding of electricity by the time of Galvani and Ampère. The Faradays and Clerk-Maxwells of psychology are still to come; new tools of investigation, we can be sure, are still to be discovered before we can penetrate much farther, just as the invention of the telescope and calculus were necessary precursors of Newton's great generalizations in mechanics.

However, even with the progress that science has already made, it is possible to give a reasonably coherent world-picture based on the scientific approach; and this contains elements of the greatest importance to our philosophy and to our practical outlook. One is that the universe is not

dualistic but monistic; another is the incorporation of
values within the scientific picture, and a reconciliation of
their absoluteness in principle with their relativity in practice; a third is the real existence of progress in evolution; a
fourth is the complete and sole responsibility of man for
achieving any further progress that may be made on this
planet, and the falsity of all his attempts to shift any of
the burden of his responsibilities onto the shoulders of outside powers; and a fifth is the establishment of the developed
human personality as the highest product of the universe
(or at least the highest product of which we have any
knowledge), with all the implications of this fact for our
social and political philosophy.

Let me take these points one by one, to show their inter-
connection. The way of advance for truth is in general the
same as the way of advance for existing life: of two alternatives, one dies out, not because the other destroys it directly,
but because it is less fitted to survive. Even after Copernicus,
the doctrine that the sun goes round the earth could still
be logically maintained. But it demanded enormous complexity of epicycle upon epicycle. The rival theory that
the earth goes round the sun was far simpler and more satisfying; in the climate provided by developing civilization it
survived, the other simply died out of human thinking.

The monistic, unitary view of the universe will survive
for the same kind of reason. Our scientific knowledge now
permits us to assert definitely that there is no break in the
continuity of phenomena. All matter, living or lifeless, is
composed of the same units—all the millions of different
lifeless substances, as well as of living species, are made
of different combinations of the chemical elements, and
these in turn of different combinations of still more elementary particles (or "wavicles"). In reproduction, there is no
moment at which life enters; there is continuity of life
between the offspring and its parent or parents. The offspring is merely a detached portion of the parental living
substance. Nowhere in the transformation of microscopic

ovum to adult human being is there a break at which one can say "here mind appears," or "there personality enters"; development is continuous.

It is the same with the vast process of organic evolution. Here, too, gradualness and continuity reign; there is no moment at which we can say that reptile ends or bird begins, no definite demarcation between man and not-man, no sharp line at which we must or indeed could postulate the sudden injection of thought or soul into evolving life. The ideas of evolution by brusque mutations of large extent have disappeared: with the new knowledge of the last twenty years the overwhelming consensus of biology has returned to support Darwin's original view of the extreme gradualness of all evolutionary change.

Nor is there the least reason for postulating any sudden injection of life into our world. Living matter is composed of the same elements as non-living, and no trace of any special "vital energy" has been detected. The scientific view is that under the conditions obtaining during the early history of the earth, the particular combination of matter that we call life was formed in the cosmic test-tube, and once formed could maintain itself by its power of self-reproduction. Any other hypothesis is less simple: the onus of proof falls on those who would maintain it.

What then becomes of the apparent dualism between matter and spirit? Many philosophers, including Professor Montague, persist in affirming that the only alternative is materialism, according to which mind is "a function of the body (matter), and depends upon it completely." This is an easy thesis to demolish; and having demolished it, they conclude that the dualistic alternative is true. However, the real alternative to dualism they have conveniently omitted to mention.

The only logical alternative to dualism is monism—that matter and mind are two aspects of one reality, that there exists one world-stuff, which reveals material or mental properties according to the point of view. Looked at from

the outside, the world-stuff has nothing but material properties; its operations appear as mind only to itself, from
within.[1] The first objection to this, that we have experience
of the minds of other people, disappears when we remember that this experience is not direct, as is the experience
of our own psychic processes, but indirect, deduced from
other people's behavior (including expression and verbal
behavior), combined with our knowledge of our own minds.
The second objection, that a dead man still has the same
body as a live one, and therefore differs by the loss of a living
soul, is still more easily disposed of. A dead body is *not* the
same as a living body: the chemical conditions in it—for
instance, the presence of enough oxygen for the functioning
of the tissues—are different. If you substitute oil for acid
in the battery of your automobile, no current will pass. The
interpretation of a primitive savage might well be that the
living soul of the contraption had fled. But we know that
the conditions have been altered: restore the old conditions
and the battery becomes "live" again. It is the same with the
body. The physicochemical conditions of the dead body are
different from those of the living body: if you could restore
the conditions found in the living body, the dead body would
live again. This has been done by artificially restarting the
heart; but owing to the rapidity with which irreversible
changes take place in dying cells, this has so far proved
possible only within a very short time after death (or, if you
prefer, what otherwise would have been death) has occurred.

But if the world-stuff is both matter and mind in one;
if there is no break in continuity between the thinking,
feeling adult human being and the inert ovum from which
he developed; no break in continuity between man and his
remote pre-amoebic ancestor; no break in continuity between
life and not-life—why, then, mind or something of the same
nature as mind must exist throughout the entire universe.
This is, I believe, the truth. We may never be able to prove
it, but it is the most economical hypothesis: it fits the facts

[1] The term *mind* is used here broadly, to denote all psychical
activity and experience, conscious or subconscious, sensory,
emotional, cognitive, and conative.

much more simply than does any dualistic theory, whether
a universal dualism or one that assumes that mind is suddenly introduced into existing matter at a certain stage,
and very much more simply than one-sided idealism (in the
metaphysical sense) or one-sided materialism.

The notion that there is something of the same nature as
human mind in lifeless matter at first sight appears incredible or ridiculous. Let us, however, illustrate its possibility
by considering certain well-established biological facts concerning electricity. Apart from lightning, the only powerful
electric phenomena known before the late eighteenth century
were the electric shocks produced by the electric eel, the
electric ray, and one or two other kinds of fish. The production of electricity by life might justly have appeared as
something rare and sporadic. However, as physiology progressed, it was found that electric currents pass when a nerve
is stimulated, when a muscle contracts, when a gland
secretes; in fact, we now know that all vital activities, of
whatever kind, from conscious thought to the fertilization
of the egg, are accompanied by some electrical activity. The
electrical charges are extremely minute and can be detected
only by the most refined instruments; but they are always
there. They are there because what we call electricity is one
aspect of all matter (indeed, when we get down to the
ultimate units of matter, such as electrons, their electrical
properties seem to be the most essential).

In the electric eel, certain muscles have been modified so
that, though they have lost their original function of con-
traction, their electric discharges are accumulated as in a
galvanic pile, and the total voltage and current are quite
respectable. Whereas in the great majority of cases the
electrical properties of living matter play no special part in
the life of the animal, they have become the specific function of the eel's electric organs: an accident of nature has
become biologically significant.

One may suggest that the same sort of thing has happened
with mind. All the activities of the world-stuff are accom-

panied by mental as well as by material happenings; in
most cases, however, the mental happenings are at such a
low level of intensity that we cannot detect them; we may
perhaps call them "psychoid" happenings, to emphasize their
difference in intensity and quality from our own psychical
or mental activities. In those organs that we call brains,
however, the psychoid activities are, in some way, made to
reinforce each other until, as is clearly the case in higher
animals, they reach a high level of intensity; and they are
the dominant and specific function of the brain of man.
Until we learn to detect psychoid activities of low intensity,
as we have learned to do with electrical happenings, we cannot prove this. But already it has become the simplest hypothesis that will fit the facts of developmental and evolutionary continuity.

In evolution, science has not merely revealed the bridge
that provides continuity between man and lifeless matter,
but has also discovered what is perhaps the most important
single biological fact yet known—the fact of evolutionary
progress. A great deal of evolution is mere diversification.
New species constantly arise, adapted to slightly different
conditions, or produced by the biological accidents of isolation or hybridization. Through this frill of diversity, however, there can be perceived a series of long-range trends,
whose course runs for millions or tens of millions of years.
The great majority of these trends are specializations. They
fit the existing type more closely to one mode of life, and in
so doing cut it off from success in others. In the evolution
of higher mammals, for instance, one line specialized as
predators, and become the carnivores; another specialized in
chewing and digesting foliage and herbage, and usually in
swift running, to become the ungulates; a third in flying—
the bats; a fourth in marine life—the whales and porpoises;
and so on. It is a universal rule that one-sided specializations
eventually come to a dead end. There is a point beyond which
natural selection cannot push them. It is impossible to be
more perfectly streamlined than a dolphin; when the horse
stock had reduced its digits to one, it could go no further;
elephants are close to the limit of weight that is possible for

an efficient land animal. When a specialization has reached
its biomechanical limit, it remains unchanged—unless new
competition causes it to become extinct. Thus most mammals
have not evolved in any important way for ten or twenty
million years, birds not for twenty or twenty-five million,
ants not for thirty million.

But besides these lines of specialization we find a few lines
whose trend is toward all-round instead of one-sided improvement; and these are not doomed to come to a stop. It is this
all-round and therefore potentially unlimited advance that
may legitimately be called progress. It is concrete and
measurable. It consists in an increased control by life over
its environment, an increased independence in relation to
the changes of that environment, an increase of knowledge,
of harmonious complexity and self-regulation.

But it is not universal or inevitable. It occurs in a few only
out of the tens of thousands of evolving types. It reveals itself
not in any advance of life as a whole, but in a raising of the
level reached by the type that is biologically dominant at
any given time. The union of many cells to form a single
individual was evolutionary progress. So was the formation of
a central nervous system, of a head, of blood circulation, of
elaborate sense-organs. Later on, emergence onto land, with
its consequent increase of self-regulation, marked a step in
progress; so did the self-regulation of temperature that we
call warm blood, the nourishment of the mammalian young
by its mother, and the steady development of intelligence
and the power to profit by experience in the mammalian
stock. The evolution by man of conceptual thought, of conscious reason and purpose, finally produced a dominant type
with radically new biological characteristics.

To assert that man is the highest product of evolution to
date is a statement of simple biological fact. There are, however, some other points concerning man's position relative
to evolutionary progress that are less obvious. First is the
curious fact that the human species is now, in all probability,
the sole repository of any possible future progress for life.
When multicellular animals first appeared, they all had

reached a new level of progress: later, some cut themselves off from further advance by entering on blind alleys, such as the fixed, vegetative existence of the polyps and corals or the headlessness and radial symmetry of the starfish and other echinoderms. The process of restriction has now, it seems, gone so far that all future progress hangs on the human germ-plasm. It is apparently a biological impossibility for any other line of life to progress into a new dominant type—not the ant, the rat, nor the ape.

Second, with the evolution of man the character of progress becomes altered. With human consciousness, values and ideals appeared on earth for the first time. The criteria of further progress must include the degree to which those ideal values are satisfied. The quest for truth and knowledge, virtue, beauty and aesthetic expression and its satisfaction through the channels of science and philosophy, mysticism and morality, literature and the arts, becomes one of the modes or avenues of evolutionary progress. A tendency in this direction had been manifested earlier in evolution. On the whole, biological progress in its later stages had been more concerned with independence of the environment than with control over it. The introduction of ideal values makes it possible for this tendency to go further. We may antici-pate that in the remote future human control over the environment will become increasingly devoted to securing greater independence—in other words, greater freedom from material exigencies—and both of them together to securing a greater degree of self-realization and of the satisfaction of human values.

It is also important to note that biological progress demands no special agency. In other words, it does not require the intervention of a conscious Divine purpose, nor the operation of some mysterious life-force or *élan vital*: like most other facts of evolution, it is the automatic result of the blind forces of reproduction, variation, and differential survival. Newton's great generalization of gravitational attrac-tion made it possible and indeed necessary to dispense with the idea of God guiding the stars in their courses; Darwin's equally great generalization of natural selection made it possible and necessary to dispense with the idea of God guiding the evolutionary courses of life. Finally, the generalizations of modern psychology and comparative religion make it possible, and necessary, to dispense with the idea of God guiding the evolutionary courses of the human species, through inspiration or other form of supernatural direction.

The present culmination of the thousand-million-year sweep of biological progress is the human species, with all its defects and mistakes. Thus the highest and richest product of the cosmic process (or, again, the highest of which we have any knowledge) is the developed human personality. It is among individual men and women that we must search for our exemplars.

A corollary of the facts of evolutionary progress is that man must not attempt to put off any of his burden of responsibility onto the shoulders of outside powers, whether these be conceived as magic or necessity, as life-force or as God. Man stands alone as the agent of his fate and the trustee of progress for life. To accept his responsibility consciously is itself an important step toward more rapid progress. Here is a field where a philosophy based on the scientific outlook is of the utmost practical importance.

But the problem that most perplexes our present age remains the question of moral certitude. As Dean Sperry says, it is the loss of the "ethical universals" with which Christianity has equipped Western civilization that creates the "grave moral perplexities" of the present. This is where modern psychology enters the picture. For a justification of our moral code we no longer have to have recourse to theological revelation, or to a metaphysical Absolute; Freud in combination with Darwin suffice to give us our philosophic vision. The great contribution of Freud was the discovery of the unconscious mind. What matter if logicians assert that the phrase is a contradiction in terms? It is now firmly established that through the process known as repression, desires and ideas, emotions and purposes, can be forced out of consciousness, or at least out of contact with the main organization of consciousness that we call the self or ego. They are then "in the unconscious," but in the unconscious they continue operating just as if they were ordinary processes of the mind, and they are still able to influence the conscious life of the ego in the most varied ways.

Repression is the banishment from consciousness of desires and ideas that produce otherwise intolerable conflict. It is a special form of what psychologists and neurologists call inhibition. The repressed ideas are so intolerable that consciousness will not even recognize their existence or examine them rationally; yet they are so powerful that they distort consciousness itself. They may manage to enter, in suitably disguised forms, into the very forces of the mind that aid in their repression, and lead to a neurotic conflict that is indefinitely prolonged. They may emerge under the guise of perversions, sublimations, compulsions, or mere oddities of behaviour. Most important for our purpose, the conflict, since it is never faced in the light of conscious reason, has to be resolved by irrational methods; emotional force must be met by emotional force. This is accomplished by the development of what psychoanalysts call the super-ego, a mental construction embodying both the repressive forces and also the feelings of guilt engendered by the conflict. From another angle, the super-ego may be looked on as the injection of external authority into the infant's developing personality, where it takes root under the form of a sense of moral compulsion. To complete the story, we may add that it is often re-projected outward, so to speak, in the form of a jealous God, an absolute moral law, an infallible Führer, or some other externalization.

The super-ego is a rationalization of the conflict between primitive unregulated impulse and the deep infantile need for dependence. It can be equated with certain aspects of conscience; it gives the compulsive force to taboos, both ritual and ethical; it provides morality with its irrational certitudes, and sometimes with an unpardoning ruthlessness; primitively, its strength is bound up with cruelty, and this issues in the idea of punishment for sin, including expiatory self-torture. It is, in fact, the non-rational and emotional element in ethics.

It has not, I think, been sufficiently recognized that repression is normal in man. Man is the only organism whose mind is so constructed that long-continued conflict is inevitable. The young child is subjected to powerful conflicts even before it can talk and reason, and long before it has adequate experience to resolve a conflict rationally. Repression is thus an adaptation to conflict, especially to early conflict; in its absence, the degree of assurance necessary for action and adjustment would be impossible.

Undoubtedly the picture of human psychology given by psychoanalysis and other modern dynamic theories is crude and incomplete, but equally undoubtedly it is a first approximation to the truth. It is as great an improvement over older theories as was mid-nineteenth-century physiology, for all its crudity, over the medieval theory of humours, or Dalton's atomic theory of chemistry, for all its incompleteness, over alchemy.

Its importance for philosophy, and especially for ethics, is enormous, for it enables us to understand how ethical and other values can be absolute in principle while remaining obstinately relative in practice; and, in conjunction with our knowledge of evolution, it enables us to reconcile absolutism and relativism by uniting them in the concept of right direction.

Values appear absolute for two reasons. The first is a result of the structure of language. The very existence of general and abstract terms like *true* and *truth* implies that an absolute Truth exists, and also that there is always an absolute difference between truth and falsehood. This, however, is not the case. Truth is only absolute when it deals with the incomplete, such as the abstractions from reality that form the basis of mathematics. The absolute difference between truth and falsehood only applies in a limited number of situations. The atomic theory of Dalton was true in giving a reasonably accurate picture of chemical fact. It was incorrect in ascribing indivisibility to atoms; but this does not make it false, only incomplete. The fact remains, however, that man's capacity for conceptual thought makes it extremely difficult for him to think in relative terms. The general and the abstract tend, almost automatically, to become invested with the intellectual halo of the absolute. The lesson of science is that this tendency should be resisted. Paradoxically, we find that we are enabled to accumulate a more complete and a more certain store of knowledge when, as in science, we reject the possibility of absolute completeness or absolute certainty, and are prepared to abandon our dearest theories in the face of new facts.

What holds for truth holds also for beauty and goodness. But in the case of goodness in particular, this predisposition to translate the particular into the general, the general into the abstract, and the abstract into the absolute, is reinforced by another effect—the sense of emotional certitude which in its origin is to be traced to the mental mechanisms growing out of the need for infantile repression. Thanks to repression, it is natural for us not only to think in absolute terms, but to feel in them. The inhibiting influences of the super-ego tend to produce an intolerant assurance of being right, because only through such an assurance could they have succeeded in repressing their opponents into the unconscious. In so far as they succeed, they acquire emotional certitude; and that emotional certitude, given the construction of the human mind, inevitably tends to rationalize itself by claiming absolute value.

When, however, we come to practice, we find ourselves plunged back into the confusion of the relative. For instance, when we win this war, what will be the right way of treating Germany? The absolute principle of justice makes us feel the demand that crime should be punished. But, applied to the Germans, does this mean punishing Hitler, the Nazi leaders, all those directly guilty of cruelty and injustice, or the whole German people? Furthermore, the absolute principle of justice conflicts with the equally absolute principles of mercy and love. And finally, these absolute emotional principles come in conflict with the frankly utilitarian principles, like the greatest good of the greatest number, whose application can only be decided rationally and relatively to circumstances. Clearly one course will prove to be more right than another; but in deciding which to adopt, the so-called absolute ethical and moral principles will only take us part of the way.

The same is true of the individual. As he grows up, he finds that his apparently absolute ethical values constantly need the assistance of relativism, in the shape of rational judgment in the light of experience, if they are to be applicable to particular situations. It is wrong to lie; but we all know circumstances where it is more wrong to tell the truth. It is wrong to take life; but it needs rational judgment to decide whether this applies to war, to certain cases of suicide and abortion, to euthanasia, to birth-control.

In fact, one of the chief tasks before each individual is to make a rational and relative adjustment of the apparent absolute of his primitive ethics, derived from infantile repression, to the practical realities of life. To accomplish this, it may even be necessary that the original structure of repressed and repressing forces be destroyed, whether by some violent emotional or religious experience, or by the deliberate "mental operation" of psychoanalysis or other form of psychotherapy.

Looked at from the evolutionary point of view, both the individual ethical values of the super-ego and the collective ones of the current system of religion and morality are adaptations enabling human life to carry on without too great a degree of incertitude and inner conflict. This means that they must have some degree of external relevance to the environment in which they arise, and are bound to change as it changes. For instance, so long as infectious disease was supposed to be a punishment for sin, it was possible to regard sacrifice to the gods as an ethical duty in times of pestilence. To-day our modern knowledge makes it ethical for us to compel the forcible isolation of sufferers from such diseases. Again, under the new conditions of Hitler's aggression and hateful methods of warfare, many convinced pacifists have changed their strong ethical belief that war is always wrong.

In the light of these facts, the dilemma of ethics begins to look rather different. The absoluteness of ethical values turns out to be apparent only, springing partly from the feeling of certitude or even compulsion associated with repression, partly from man's natural yearning for certitude, partly from his language habits. On the other hand, the inconstancy of ethical values revealed by history and anthropology, which is at first so confusing and distressing, turns out not to be wholly at random. Ethics is related, though incompletely and indirectly, to the solid facts of man's environment: it is a social adaptation.

The task before us, as ethical beings, now begins to take shape. It is to preserve the force of ethical conviction that springs up naturally out of infantile dependence and the need for inhibition and repression in early life, but to see that it is applied, under the correctives of reason and experience, to provide the most efficient and the most desirable moral framework for living. This will undoubtedly mean radical changes in the early upbringing of children, as well as in the methods of education and in accepted religions and codes of ethics. For instance, sociologists realize that existing ethico-religious systems often contain a large element of psychological compensation: they compensate for the miseries of this world with the bliss of a world to come, they compensate for ignorance of fact with certitude of feeling, they compensate for actual imperfections of ethical practice by setting up impossible ethical ideals. This is not merely hypocrisy; it is a primitive method of self-defence against a hard and difficult reality.

Again, it is becoming clear that harshness of punishment in early life tends to the development of a morally vindictive super-ego: other methods are required for the development of a character where the aggressive and sadistic impulses are kept subordinate. The most difficult lesson to learn is that irrational and intolerant certitude is undesirable.

We have seen how this applies to truth: the lesson is difficult
there also, but science has learned it. It will be even more
difficult to learn in ethics: but it must be learned if we are
to emerge from psychological barbarism. To cling to certitude is to prolong an infantile reaction beyond the period
when it is necessary. To become truly adult, we must learn
to bear the burden of incertitude.

Another serious difficulty is how to arouse strong ethical
feeling on important moral issues. It is easy to feel strongly
about sexual behaviour, because almost inevitably certain
components of the sexual impulse become repressed in early
life—so easy, in fact, that "morality" is often used to mean
sexual morality alone. But it is much harder to feel strongly
about social problems such as malnutrition or unemployment, because the connection with the repressive mechanism
is not so automatic. However, through education and general
social attitude such problems could be linked with a strong
feeling about the wrongness of cruelty, a feeling which in
its turn is readily generated by the repression of the aggressive impulses. In addition, of course, the child's natural sense
of sympathy can be appealed to and strengthened, and
primitive feelings of aggression can be sublimated and
canalized into constructive activities. But any strong emotional sense of absolute wrongness can only be introduced
by utilizing the fact of repression, with its accompanying
load of guilt. Society must make rational use of an irrational
mechanism to create the system of values it wants.

I would draw some such general conclusion as this. A
scientifically based philosophy enables us in the first place
to cease tormenting ourselves with questions that ought not
to be asked because they cannot be answered—such as
questions about a First Cause, or Creation, or Ultimate
Reality. Secondly, it encourages us to think in terms of
right direction and optimum speed in place of complete but
static solutions. At the present moment, for instance, it is
much more essential to know that we are moving with
reasonable speed toward certain general types of superna-

tional co-operation than to nail some elaborate blue-print of international organization to our masthead. Thirdly, it is capable of giving man a much truer picture of his nature and his place in the universe than any other philosophic approach. Man is now the dominant biological type, and the developed human individual the highest product of the cosmic process that we know. That is a proud piece of knowledge. It is tempered by the reflection that very few human individuals realize a fraction of their possibilities, and that in a large proportion passive or active evil predominates. But the knowledge has important practical bearings. Once we realize that the development of individuals is the ultimate yardstick by which to measure human progress, we can see more clearly how to formulate our aims for the world after the war.

The fact that we, all the human beings now in existence, are the exclusive trustees for carrying any further the progress already achieved by life is a responsibility which, if sobering, is also inspiring; as is the fact that we have no longer either the intellectual or the moral right to shift any of this responsibility from our own shoulders to those of God or any other outside power. Indeed, the problem that appears to be the most perplexing and distressing turns out, in the light of a thoroughgoing scientific approach, to be full of encouragement. I mean the problem of ethical and other values. We have been accustomed to think of these as a scaffolding for our morals, conveniently run up for us by some outside agency. Now that this is no longer possible, we feel bewildered, unable to conceive of any firm moral construction in which we can abide. The truth, however, as shown by the extension of scientific method into individual and social psychology, is that we create our own values. Some we generate consciously; some subconsciously; and some only indirectly, through the structure of the societies in which we live. Through a fuller comprehension of these mechanisms we shall be able to guide and accelerate this process of value creation, which is not only essential for our individual lives but basic to the achieving of true evolutionary progress in the future.

WAR AS A BIOLOGICAL PHENOMENON

WHENEVER we tend to become completely absorbed in an enterprise or an idea, it is a good thing to stand off from it now and again and look at it from the most dispassionate point of view possible. War is no exception. Quite rightly, all our major efforts must to-day be devoted to the urgent business of making sure that we win the war and win it as quickly as possible. We are for most purposes immersed in the war; however, it will not merely do no harm, but will actually be of service, if now and again we try to get outside it and to look at it as objectively as we can in long perspective.

The longest possible perspective is that of the biologist, to whom man is a single animal species among hundreds of thousands of others, merely one of the products (albeit the latest and the most successful) of millions of years of evolution.

How does war look when pinned out in the biologist's collection? In the first place, he is able to say with assurance that war is not a general law of life, but an exceedingly rare biological phenomenon. War is not the same thing as conflict or bloodshed. It means something quite definite:— an organized physical conflict between groups of one and the same species. Individual disputes between members of the same species are not war, even if they involve bloodshed and death. Two stags fighting for a harem of hinds, or a man murdering another man, or a dozen dogs fighting over a bone, are not engaged in war. Competition between two different species, even if it involves physical conflict, is not war. When the brown rat was accidentally brought to Europe and proceeded to oust the black rat from most of its haunts, that was not war between the two species of rat; nor is it war in any but a purely metaphorical sense when we speak of making war on the malaria mosquito or the boll-weevil. Still less is it war when one species preys upon another, even when the preying is done by an organized group. A pack of wolves attacking a flock of sheep or deer, or a peregrine killing a duck, is not war. Much of nature, as Tennyson correctly said, is "red in tooth and claw"; but this only means what it says, that there is a great deal of killing in the animal world, not that war is the rule of life.

In point of fact, there are only two kinds of animals that habitually make war—man and ants. Even among ants war is mainly practised by one group, comprising only a few species among the tens of thousands that are known to science. They are the harvester ants, inhabitants of arid regions where there is little to pick up during the dry months. Accordingly they collect the seeds of various grasses at the end of the growing season and store them in special underground granaries in their nests. It is these reserve supplies which are the object of ant warfare. The inhabitants of one nest set out deliberately to raid the supplies of another group. According to Forel and other patient students of ant life, they may employ quite elaborate military tactics, and the battles generally result in heavy casualties. If the attackers win, they remove the stores grain by grain to their own nest. Ant wars never last nearly so long as human wars. One campaign observed by the American myrmecologist McCook in Penn Square in the centre of Philadephia, lasted almost 3 weeks. The longest on record is 6½ weeks.

Harvesters are the only kind of ants to go in for accumulating property, as well as the chief kind to practise war. This association of property with war is interesting, as various anthropologists believe that in the human species war, or at any rate habitual and organized war, did not arise in human evolution until man had reached the stage of settled civilization, when he began to accumulate stores of grain and other forms of wealth.

Less deliberate wars may also occur in some other species, between communities whose nests are so close that they compete for the same food-territory. When similarly provoked conflicts occur between closely related species, the term war may perhaps be extended to them. On the other hand, the raids of the slave-making ants are not true war, but a curious combination of predation and parasitism.

There is another group of ants called army ants, which suggests military activity; but the phrase is really a mis-nomer, for these army ants are in reality simply predatory species which happen to hunt in packs: they are the wolves of the insect world, not the war-mongers.

So much then for war as a biological phenomenon. The facts speak for themselves. War, far from being a universal law of nature, or even a common occurrence, is a very rare exception among living creatures; and where it occurs, it is either associated with another phenomenon, almost equally rare, the amassing of property, or with territorial rights.

Biology can help put war in its proper perspective in another way. War has often been justified on biological grounds. The progress of life, say war's apologists, depends on the struggle for existence. This struggle is universal, and results in what Darwin called "Natural Selection," and this in its turn results in the "Survival of the Fittest." Natural Selection, of course, works only in a mass way, so that those which survive in the struggle will merely have an average of fitness a little above those which perish or fail to repro-duce themselves. But some of the qualities which make for success in the struggle, and so for a greater chance of sur-vival, will certainly be inherited; and since the process con-tinues generation after generation not merely for thousands but for millions of years, the average fitness and efficiency of the race will steadily and continuously be raised until it can be pushed no higher. In any case, say the believers in this doctrine, struggle is necessary to maintain fitness; if the pressure of competition and conflict is removed, biological efficiency will suffer, and degeneration will set in.

Darwin's principle of Natural Selection, based as it is on constant pressure of competition or struggle, has been invoked to justify various policies in human affairs. For instance, it was used, especially by politicians in late Victorian England, to justify the principles of *laisser-faire* and free competition in business and economic affairs. And it was used, especially by German writers and politicians from the late nineteenth century onwards, to justify militarism. War, so ran this particular version of the argument, is the form which is taken by Natural Selection and the Struggle for Existence in the affairs of the nations. Without war, the heroic virtues degenerate; without war, no nation can possibly become great or successful.

It turns out, however, that both the *laisser-faire* economists and the militarists were wrong in appealing to biology for justification of their policies. War is a rather special aspect of competition between members of the same species—what biologists call "intra-specific competition." It is a special case because it involves physical conflict and often the death of those who undertake it, and also because it is physical conflict not between individuals but between organized groups; yet it shares certain properties in common with all other forms of intra-specific struggle or competition. And recent studies of the way in which Natural Selection works and how the Struggle for Existence operates in different conditions have resulted in this rather surprising but very important conclusion—that intra-specific competition need not, and usually does not, produce results of any advantage to the species as a whole.

A couple of examples will show what I mean. In birds like the peacock or the argus pheasant, the males are polygamous—if they can secure a harem. They show off their gorgeous plumage before the hen birds in an elaborate and very striking display, at definite assembly grounds where males and females go for the purpose of finding mates. The old idea that the hen deliberately selects the male she thinks the most beautiful is putting the matter in human terms which certainly do not apply to a bird's mind; but it seems

certain that the brilliant and exciting display does have an
effect on the hen bird, stimulating her to greater readiness to
mate. Individual male birds meet with different degrees of
success in this polygamous love business: some secure quite
a number of mates, others only one or a few, and some get
none at all. This puts an enormous biological premium on
success: the really successful male leaves many times more
descendants than the unsuccessful. Here, then, is Natural
Selection working at an exceedingly high pitch of intensity
to make the display plumage and display actions more
effective in their business of stimulating the hens. Accordingly, in polygamous birds of this kind, we often find the
display plumage developed to a fantastic extent, even so far
as to be a handicap to the species as a whole. Thus the
display organ of the peacock, his train of enormously over-
grown tail-covert feathers, is so long and cumbersome that it
is a real handicap in flight. In the argus pheasant the chief
display organs are the beautifully adorned wings which the
male throws up and forward in display so that he looks like
a gigantic bell-shaped flower. The business of display has
been so important that it has overridden the business of
flying, and now the male argus pheasant can fly only with
difficulty, a few feet at a time.

Here are two good examples of how a purely intra-specific
struggle, in this case between individual rival males, can
produce results which are not merely useless but harmful
to the species as a whole in its struggle for existence against
its enemies and the forces of nature. In general, selection for
success in reproduction reaches greater intensities than
selection for individual survival, for the simple reason that
reproduction implies multiplication: the individual is a
single unit, but, as we have just seen for polygamous birds,
success in reproduction may give the individual's characteristics a multiple representation in later generations.

In flowering plants, the intra-specific struggle for reproduction between different individuals often produces results
which, if not directly harmful to the species, are at least
incredibly wasteful. We need only think of the fantastic

profusion of bloom on flowering trees like dogwood or haw-
thorn or catalpa, or the still more fantastic profusion of pollen
in trees which rely on fertilization by the wind, like pine
and fir. The individual trees are competing for the privilege
of surviving in their descendants; the species could certainly
perpetuate itself with a much more modest expenditure of
living material.

One final example. Naturalists have often noted the almost
unbelievable perfection of the protective resemblance of
certain insects to their surroundings. The most extraordinary
cases are the resemblances of various butterflies, like the
Kallima, to dead leaves. Not only do the folded wings perfectly resemble a dead leaf in shape and colour, not only do
they have a projection to imitate the stalk, and dark lines
which perfectly simulate the veins, but some even go so far
as to be marked with imitation mould-spots and holes!

Now, in all butterflies the survival of the species depends
to a preponderant degree on the capacity of the defenceless
and juicy caterpillar and chrysalis to survive. Selection
presses with much greater intensity on the larval and pupal
stages than on the adult. Furthermore, there is some sort of
balance between the number of adults which survive to
reproduce themselves and the intensity of selection which
presses on the next generation of caterpillars. If more adults
reproduce, there will be many more caterpillars, and they
will be more easily found by their enemies, especially the
tiny parasitic wasps which lay eggs inside the caterpillars,
the eggs growing into grubs which devour the unfortunate
animals from within. Conversely, if fewer adults reproduce,
there are many fewer caterpillars, but each of them has a
better chance of surviving to the butterfly stage. Accordingly,
the protection of the adults is, from the point of view of the
species, a secondary matter. Of course they must be protected
sufficiently well for a reasonable number to survive and
reproduce, but after this it is quite unimportant—for the
species—if a slightly higher or a slightly lower proportion
survives.

It is unimportant for the species but it remains important for the individual. If one kind of adult is better protected than another, it will automatically leave a higher average number of offspring; and so the intra-specific struggle for reproduction among the individual adult butterflies will continue to push any protective devices they possess on toward ever greater efficiency, even though this may be quite immaterial to the survival of the species. The perfection of the Kallima's resemblance to a dead leaf is one of the marvels of nature; not the least marvelous part of it is that it is of no value to the species as a whole.

On the other hand, intra-specific competition and struggle need not always lead to results which are useless to the species. The competition between individuals may concern qualities which are also useful in the struggle of the species against its enemies, as in deer or zebra or antelope—the same extra turn of speed which gives one individual an advantage over another in escaping from wolf or lion or cheetah will also stand the whole species in good stead. Or it may concern qualities which help the species in surviving in a difficult environment; an extra capacity for resisting drought in an individual cactus or yucca will help the species in colonizing new and more arid regions. It will not be useless or harmful to the species unless the competition is directed solely or mainly against other individuals like itself.

Furthermore, the results will differ according to conditions. When there is competition for mates among male birds, it will become really intense only when polygamy prevails and the advantage of success is therefore multiplied. Monogamous birds also stimulate their mates with a display of bright plumage, but in this case the display plumage is never developed to a pitch at which it is actually harmful in the general struggle for existence: the balance is struck at a different level.

All these considerations apply to war. In the first place it is obvious that war is an example of intra-specific competi-

tion—it is a physical conflict between groups within the
same species. As such, it might be not merely useless but
harmful to the species as a whole—a drag on the evolutionary progress of humanity. But, further, it might turn out to
be harmful in some conditions and not in others. This indeed
seems to be the truth. Those who say that war is always
and inevitably harmful to humanity are indulging in an
unjustified generalization (though not nearly so unjustified
as the opposite generalization of the militarists who say that
war is both necessary and beneficial to humanity). Warfare between peoples living on the tribal level of early
barbarism may quite possibly have been on balance a good
thing for the species—by encouraging the manly virtues,
by mixing the heritage of otherwise closed communities
through the capture of women, by keeping down excessive
population-pressure, and in other ways. War waged by small
professional armies according to a professional code, was at
least not a serious handicap to general progress. But long-
continued war in which the civilian population is starved,
oppressed, and murdered and whole countries are laid waste,
as in the Thirty Years War—that is harmful to the species;
and so is total war in the modern German sense in which
entire populations may be enslaved and brutalized, as with
Poland or Greece to-day, whole cities smashed, like Rotter-
dam, the resources of large regions deliberately destroyed,
as in the Ukraine. The more total war becomes, both
intensively, as diverting more of the energies of the population from construction to destruction, and extensively, as
involving more and more of the countries of the globe, the
more of a threat does it become to the progress of the human
species. As H. G. Wells and many others have urged, it
might even turn back the clock of civilization and force the
world into another Dark Age. War of this type is an intra-
specific struggle from which nobody, neither humanity at
large nor any of the groups engaged in the conflict, can
really reap any balance of advantage, though of course we
may snatch particular advantages out of the results of war.

But it is one thing to demonstrate that modern war is harmful to the species, another thing to do something about abolishing it. What has the biologist to say to those who assert that war is inevitable, since, they say, it is a natural outcome of human nature and human nature cannot possibly be changed?

To this the biologist can give a reassuring answer. War is not an inevitable phenomenon of human life; and when objectors of this type talk of human nature they really mean the expression of human nature, and this can be most thoroughly changed.

As a matter of observable fact, war occurs in certain conditions and not in others. There is no evidence of prehistoric man's having made war, for all his flint implements seem to have been designed for hunting, for digging, or for scraping hides; and we can be pretty sure that even if he did, any wars between groups in the hunting stage of human life would have been both rare and mild. Organized warfare is most unlikely to have begun before the stage of settled civilization. In man, as in ants, war in any serious sense is bound up with the existence of accumulations of property to fight about.

However, even after man had learned to live in cities and amass property, war does not seem to have been inevitable. The early Indus civilization, dating from about 3000 B.C., reveals no traces of war. There seem to have been periods in early Chinese history, as well as in the Inca civilization in Peru, in which war was quite or almost absent.

As for human nature, it contains no specific war instinct, as does the nature of harvester ants. There is in man's make-up a general aggressive tendency, but this, like all other human urges, is not a specific and unvarying instinct; it can be moulded into the most varied forms. It can be canalized into competitive sport, as in our own society, or as when certain Filipino tribes were induced to substitute football for head-hunting. It can be sublimated into non-competitive sport, like mountain-climbing, or into higher types of activity altogether, like exploration or research or social crusades.

There is no theoretical obstacle to the abolition of war. But do not let us delude ourselves with the idea that this will be easy. The first step needed is the right kind of international machinery. To invent that will not be particularly simple: sanctions against aggressors, the peaceful reconciliation of national interests in a co-operative international system, an international police force—we can see in principle that these and other necessary bits of anti-war machinery are possible, but it will take a great deal of hard thinking to design them so that they will really work.

The second step is a good deal more difficult. It is to find what William James called a "moral equivalent for war," while at the same time reducing the reservoir of potential aggressiveness which now exists in every powerful nation. This is a psychological problem. Thanks to Freud and modern psychology in general, we are now beginning to understand how the self-assertive impulses of the child may be frustrated and repressed in such a way as to drive them underground. There in the subconscious they may persist in the form of crude urges to aggression and cruelty, which are all the more dangerous for not being consciously recognized.

To prevent the accumulation of this store of psychological dynamite and to find ways in which our self-assertive impulses can issue along conscious and constructive channels is a big job. It means a better structure of social and family life, one which does not inflict such frustrations on the growing human personality; it means a new approach to education; it means providing outlets in the form of physical or mental adventure for the impulses which would otherwise be unused even if not repressed. It is a difficult task; but by no means an impossible one.

Thus in the perspective of biology war first dwindles to the status of a rare curiosity. Further probing, however, makes it loom larger again. For one thing, it is a form of intra-specific struggle, and as such may be useless or even harmful to the species as a whole. Then we find that one of the very few animal species which make war is man; and man is to-day not merely the highest product of evolution, but the only type still capable of real evolutionary progress. And war, though it need not always be harmful to the human species and its progress, indubitably is so when conducted in the total fashion which is necessary in this technological age. Thus war is not merely a human problem; it is a biological problem of the broadest scope, for on its abolition may depend life's ability to continue the progress which it has slowly but steadily achieved through more than a thousand million years.

But the biologist can end on a note of tempered hope. War is not inevitable for man. His aggressive impulses *can* be canalized into other outlets; his political machinery *can* be designed to make war less likely. These things *can* be done: but to do them will require a great deal of hard thinking and hard work. While waging this particular war with all our might, we have a duty to keep a corner of our minds open, engaged on the job of thinking out ways and means of preventing war in general in the future.

DARWINISM TO-DAY

DARWIN'S great book, *The Origin of Species*, comprised two quite distinct elements. In the first place, it demonstrated, with a vast wealth of examples, that the current theory of the fixity of species was untenable, whether in its theological guise of special creation or in any other form; it simply would not fit the facts of nature. The facts of nature demanded an evolutionary theory: gradual change was the rule in life, constantly producing new types—not only new species, but also larger groups of every degree. In the second place, Darwin proposed a mechanism to account for evolution—the theory of Natural Selection, by which favourable varieties would automatically be accumulated and the apparent purposefulness of life could be accounted for in straightforward mechanistic terms.

It was this latter element which gave Darwin's work its influence among professional biologists. Many of them were ripe for conversion to the idea of evolution, but before 1859 no one had put forward any but the most improbable suggestions as to how evolution could have been brought about. T. H. Huxley, for instance, records how, when he read the *Origin*, he said to himself "How stupid of me not to have thought of that!" and from then on became the champion of Darwinism.

This Darwinian view of evolution was generally accepted by biologists in the latter part of last century. But about 1890 doubts began to be thrown upon it, and around 1910 it had become so unfashionable that some critics proclaimed the death of Darwinism. By Darwinism, of course, was meant the selectionist theory of the method of evolution: the fact that evolution has occurred was never seriously questioned by biologists after 1859, except by a few survivors from the pre-Darwinian period, and a very few later cranks.

This sceptical attitude of the early twentieth century was

due to two main causes. For one thing, orthodox Darwinism was tending to become purely speculative, invoking natural selection to explain anything and everything without requiring proof and without providing any explanation of the machinery by which the results could be brought about. For another, genetics had discovered the fact of mutation—in other words, that hereditary change proceeds by jumps; and the theory was advanced that evolution proceeded by large jumps; not by the gradual change which was the keystone of Darwin's view.

In the last twenty-five years, however, an enormous amount of new facts about evolution and heredity have been discovered, and the balance has now swung over heavily, and, I think, permanently, in favour of Darwinism or selectionism. Chief among these new facts is the discovery that most mutations are not large, but very small steps of change.

It turns out that the reports of the death of Darwinism, like those of the death of Mark Twain, were very much exaggerated. Indeed, the net result of the last quarter century's work in biology has been the re-establishment of natural selection as the essential method of evolution, and its re-establishment not merely where Darwin left it, but on a far more secure footing. For one thing, the alternative explanations have ceased to be plausible. First among these is Lamarckism, or the so-called inheritance of acquired characters (which means the inheritance of characters acquired by an individual as a result of changes in the environment, like tanning due to sun, or of use or disuse of organs, like the more powerful muscles of the athlete or heavy worker; it does not refer to characters "acquired" through new mutation). This has now been thoroughly discredited. It has been definitely disproved in a number of cases; it cannot in any case apply to a large range of facts (such as the evolution of the hard skeleton of higher insects, or of our own teeth); the apparent examples of its existence have all been shown either to be due to error or susceptible of an alternative explanation; and it is logically self-contradictory.

Second, there is orthogenesis, or evolution in a prede-
termined direction, supposedly due to the germ-plasm being
predestined to vary only in a certain way. It is true that
when we can trace the actual course of evolution by means
of abundant fossils, we often find that it does proceed in
straight lines. The most familiar example is the steady evolution of the horse toward speed and the one-toed foot and
toward elaborate teeth for grinding grass—but wherever
(as is in most cases obvious) the direction is toward greater
efficiency, this is to be expected on the basis of natural
selection. In any case, there are some examples, like that
of the elephants or the baboons, where evolution is not in
a straight line, but changes direction during its course.
There are a few puzzling cases, like the trend toward apparently useless or harmful characters, as seen in a number of
groups of Ammonites shortly before their final extinction;
but they are quite exceptional, and may prove to be susceptible of alternative explanation. In any case, orthogenesis in a
useless (or harmful) direction would demand mutation-
rates much higher than any yet found in nature.

There are also the vitalistic theories of a mysterious life-
force or unconscious purpose, like Bergson's *élan vital*.
However, these are in reality not explanations at all, but
mere confessions of ignorance. To say that life evolves
because of an *élan vital* is on a par with saying that a loco-
motive runs because of an *élan locomotif*.

Not only have the alternative explanations become
implausible, but a great deal of new support has been
forthcoming for the theory of natural selection. One of Darwin's difficulties about his own theory (which caused him to
give greater weight to Lamarckism than he would otherwise
have done) was that he could not see how new hereditary
variations of small extent—what we to-day should call small
mutations—could be preserved and kept from being swamped
by crossing. This, as R. A. Fisher has pointed out, was due
to his acceptance of the idea, current in his time, of "blend-
ing inheritance." In a cross between two distinct types, the
material bases of their heredity (and Darwin's generation

completely lacked concrete knowledge on this subject) were
supposed to blend in the resultant offspring, as two drops of
coloured ink will blend with each other. Thus, any new
character would be quite literally diluted on crossing with
the original type, and would soon fade out. The essence
of Mendelism, however, is that the genes or units of heredity
remain unchanged (apart from rare mutation), however
they are combined with other genes. Many of the new genes
produced by mutation can remain in the germ-plasm indefinitely until conditions are favourable, when they will
begin to increase their representation in the stock. If a new
mutant gene is recessive—i.e. must appear in double dose
before it produces any visible effect—it can be carried in
single dose for an indefinite period, even if it is slightly
deleterious.

What is more, we now know that the effects of genes
can be markedly altered by other genes, and numerous
examples exist where slightly deleterious genes have been
rendered harmless or even beneficial by being "buffered,"
in the chemist's phraseology, by new combinations of other
genes. A beautiful example comes from domestic dogs. In
producing the show type of St. Bernard, man has encouraged
features characteristic of abnormal overgrowth of the pituitary gland: yet St. Bernards are not themselves abnormal,
as a man with comparable characteristics would be. However,
when St. Bernards are crossed with other breeds like Great
Danes, a considerable number of the offspring show actual
pathological symptoms. In producing his ideal of a St. Bernard, man has selected for genes making the pituitary
abnormal: but he has also aimed at healthy dogs and so has
automatically selected for other genes which would prevent
the genes influencing the pituitary from exerting any major
harmful effect. But when these "buffering" genes are diluted
or reduced in number by crossing, the potential abnormality
of the pituitary can become actual.

This fact of recombination is the source of a whole category of variation unsuspected by Darwin; much that is new

in evolution is due, not to wholly new genes produced by mutation, but only to new combinations of old genes.

To sum up, most of the raw material of evolution is produced in the first instance by mutation of genes into new forms. Owing to the fact that they are not blended in crosses, this new variation does not have to be accepted or rejected immediately, but can be stored in reserve, so to speak. If not acceptable in itself, it can even be rendered acceptable by combination with other genes. And, in the second place, recombination of old genes is capable of producing a large further supply of new variation.

Still another fraction of the raw material of evolution depends on the fact that the genes are arranged in a row along a series of visible (but of course microscopic) thread-like bodies called the chromosomes. Owing to accidents in cell reproduction, whole sets of chromosomes may be added or subtracted. Doubling of the normal complement of chromosomes is a frequent subsidiary method of evolution in plants. The polyploids, as the types with increased chromosome-number are called, are often more resistant to extreme conditions: for instance, polyploids constitute an unusually large proportion of the varieties found in the arctic and mountain regions that have become recolonized since the retreat of the ice after the Ice Age.

Chromosome-doubling may also occur after a cross between two true species. In this case, a new species is formed at one jump—a process which would have shocked most of Darwin's nineteenth-century followers, who believed that all evolution was gradual. Sometimes such new types are weakly, and die out: in other cases the new combination of genes gives them exceptional vigour, and they may even oust both their parents. The classical example of this comes from the rice-grasses, *Spartina*, which live on mud-flats. During the last half-century a new type of rice-grass appeared in Western Europe, and has been so successful that the Dutch have used it to reclaim land from the sea. Investigation has proved that this is a new polyploid species produced by the crossing of an original European species with one accidentally imported from America. In some areas the European species has been virtually exterminated by the new type.

Another instance is the crossing of the two poppies *Papaver nudicaule* and *P. striatocarpum*, the offspring of which are quite distinct from either parent, are fully fertile, and breed true.

Single chromosomes or groups of them may also be added or subtracted to give favourable results: a cytological accident of this sort·gave rise, it seems, to the very successful branch of the rose family which later produced the apples and pears and their relatives.

Finally, bits of chromosomes may be shifted about. Small sections may be repeated, thus increasing the total number of genes available. Sections may be inverted, a process which tends to isolate the genes they contain from those contained in the uninverted section. Or chromosomes may exchange sections, which will help in the reproductive isolation of the new strain.

All these kinds of chromosome mutations, too, provide a source of variation unknown to Darwin, thus helping to account for the almost incredible profusion of distinct species in life (nearly a million in insects alone!). But the most important raw material of evolution seems to consist of gene mutations. In the early days of Mendelism the existence of mutation was taken to mean evolution by big jumps, and to run counter to Darwin's conception of steady and gradual change. This, however, was merely due to the fact that attention was, quite naturally, first concentrated on those mutations which could be readily detected—in other words, those with large effects. Just because they have large effects, however, they are apt to throw the hereditary machinery out of gear, and so not to be of much value for evolution. Later, it was discovered that the majority of gene mutations are of small extent, often quite difficult of detection save by the most refined techniques. And the accumulation of such small mutations, constantly buffered by new recombinations, will give precisely the type of change that Darwin had in mind. Evolution does go by jumps, but in most cases the jumps are so small that they hardly ever take the new type outside the range of variation already existing in the species, and the visible result is a gradual one. Discontinuity of variation is thus translated by selection into continuity of evolutionary change: life marches up a ramp, not a staircase.

So much for the mechanism of evolution. But Darwin was almost equally unprovided with knowledge about the actual course pursued by evolution in different groups and in different conditions. He was aware of the fact that fossils from an earlier epoch differed from the modern inhabitants of the region, though resembling them in general type; he was aware that isolation might play a role in the production of new species; he knew of animal or plant groups which were on the border-line between a mere variety and an obviously "good" species; he worked out for himself some of the results to be expected of sexual selection (i.e. competition for mates between rival males). But that, together with the indirect evidence provided by comparative anatomy and geographical distribution, was about all.

With this meagre body of knowledge at his disposal, his genius was able to put evolution on the map; but he could not proceed to the further task of mapping evolution itself. That was reserved for the slow cumulative work of several later generations of biologists.

It is not easy to sum up the chief results of that later work in brief and intelligible form; but it must be attempted. First, there is the formation of new species. These, we now know, originate in many different ways, and even those with the same type of origin may come to differ later in size and internal structure. The chief method of origin is through physical isolation. Once two groups are physically isolated so that they can no longer interbreed, they inevitably come to diverge from each other in the new mutations and the new gene-recombinations which they accumulate under the influence of natural selection. And after a certain time the differences in their constitution reach such a pitch that, even if the two stocks are brought together once more, they are partially or wholly infertile on crossing.

In addition, when an isolated group is small in numbers, it can be shown on mathematical grounds that it is likely to pick up and incorporate some mutations and recombinations that are useless or even slightly unfavourable. Thus, some of the diversity of life is, biologically speaking, purely accidental.

These effects, both of physical isolation and of small populations, are well illustrated by the plants and animals of islands. A population on an island is more or less completely isolated from other groups: and, accordingly, islands have a disproportionate number of distinctive sub-species and species, different from the species inhabiting the nearest mainland and from those inhabiting other near-by islands.

The extraordinary number of distinctive species of giant tortoises and of ground-finches on the Galapagos archipelago was one of the main facts met with by Darwin in his voyage on H.M.S. *Beagle* which convinced him of the reality of evolution. Again, there is only one form of mouse-deer on the whole of Sumatra and Borneo, while the Rhio-Linga archipelago close by, with only $\frac{1}{150}$th of the area, boasts no less than seven distinct sub-species.

In the Adriatic a large number of islands have been formed by subsidence of the land since the end of the Ice Age. Many of them are inhabited by distinctive races of lizards. A recent study has shown that the smaller the island, and therefore the smaller its lizard population, the more different this has become from the mainland type from which it was originally derived (see Table).

The other chief method by which new species are formed is through genetic isolation. This happens when a new form, wholly or partly infertile when crossed with its parent, is produced by some genetic accident—by means of the reduplication of whole chromosome sets, with or without previous species-hybridization; by means of the subtraction

DIFFERENTIATION IN ISLAND LIZARDS

area (arbitrary units)	0–6	6–12	12–18	18–24	24–30	30–36	depth (m)
<0·5	2½		2½				
0·5–1	1	1					
1–5	1, 2	1, 2	2, 2½, 2½, 3	3		4	
5–10	1						
10–100	0		2				
100–1000			0				

Table showing the influence of time and of size of population on the differentiation of island lizards from the mainland form. The depth is the maximum depth of water between the island and the mainland; as the islands have been formed by subsidence, the depth gives a measure of the time since isolation occurred. The area represents the area of the island, which is a measure of the population. The figures 1-4 in the chequerboard represent degrees of difference of the island forms from the mainland form. It will be seen that on the whole the longer the time of isolation and the smaller the size of the population, the greater is the degree of divergence. (Reproduced by kind permission of the publishers of J. S. Huxley's *Evolution: the Modern Synthesis*, Messrs. Allen & Unwin.)

or addition of whole chromosomes; or, in some cases, by the breakage of chromosomes and the reunion of the pieces in new arrangements.

The result is an overwhelming multiplicity of distinct species. Naturally they are all adapted to their surroundings: but the geographical and cytological accidents that produced physical and genetic isolation causes their number to be much greater than that which would be necessary on purely adaptive grounds; and non-adaptive variation adds its quota to the diversity.

Most of evolution is thus what we may call short-term diversification. But this kaleidoscopic change is shot through with a certain proportion of long-term diversification in the shape of the long-range trends revealed in fossils by the palaeontologist and deduced from comparative studies by the morphologist. These trends are almost all of them one-sided specializations, each one exploiting a particular mode of life. Thus, both reptiles and mammals, beginning with small and generalized creatures, radiated out into specialized lines including carnivores, herbivores, climbing forms, flying forms, and aquatic forms. Every possible niche is filled; some trends even involve degeneration, such as the trend of the barnacles from a free-living, shrimp-like creature to a sedentary life, or of other active crustacea to an existence as shapeless parasites.

These trends may continue for a very long time—up to tens of millions of years: but they always come at last to a dead end. After this, minor diversification may continue at the species level, but no further improvement takes place in the major specialization. Thus, birds ceased to show any improvement as flying mechanisms some 15 million years ago, and there has been no evolutionary improvement of the ant type for perhaps 25 or 30 million years.

Such trends in a given direction are to be expected on Darwinian principles. Improvement of teeth and claws for a carnivorous existence, for instance, will be an advantage to a small generalized mammal when there are no specialized carnivorous mammalian competitors already in the field, and will be favoured by natural selection. And once the type has become at all adapted to flesh-eating, it will be almost impossible for it to switch over to a herbivorous existence, for example: the number of mutations needed is much too great, and meanwhile any single mutation making for greater efficiency as a carnivore will be caught in the net of natural selection and incorporated in the constitution of the stock. The stock thus finds itself at the bottom of an evolutionary groove of specialization. Natural selection forces it farther along in the same direction, while constantly deepening the groove and so making it ever more impossible for the stock to escape out of it into some other way of life. The dead end comes when the specialization is so near its maximum possible perfection that selection cannot force the stock any further.

A third and still rarer type of change is evolutionary progress, which escapes the dead end awaiting specialization. It does so because its essence is all-round improvement, as opposed to the one-sided improvement that characterizes all specialization. It raises the general level of life's performance, instead of merely improving performance in respect of one particular mode of existence. The development of a head and brain or of a blood-system were early steps in progressive evolution, while the acquisition of "warm blood" and so of a constant internal temperature, or the gradual development in mammals of higher mental faculties such as association and the capacity for learning by experience, are later examples.

The net result of evolutionary progress can be defined as the raising of the upper level attained by life in respect of certain very general properties—greater control; greater independence; greater harmony of construction; greater capacity for knowledge (and, we may probably add, for emotion). More concretely, it has permitted the rise of a succession of what the biologist calls dominant groups, because they spread and evolve rapidly, cause the extinction of many representatives of other groups, and play a new and predominant role on the evolutionary stage. The last three dominant groups in life's history have been the reptiles, the mammals, and man, each later one arising from an unspecialized branch of the one before. Most (or, in some cases, all) the branches of a dominant group undergo specialization, and then eventually come to a dead end, either by ceasing to evolve, or by the still deader end of complete extinction, as with most of the reptilian specializations, like the Dinosaurs, Ichthyosaurs, and Pterodactyls.

I said that progressive lines were rare. If we define progress strictly as capacity for unlimited further avoidance of dead ends, there has only been one progressive line in the whole of evolution—that which has led in its later stages through fish, amphibian, reptile, and mammal to man; for it appears established that all other lines have come to an evolutionary dead end well before the later part of the tertiary period.

Thus, in the broad view, evolution as a process consists of one line of unlimited progress among thousands of long-range trends toward specialization, each of these latter in turn beset with a frill, so to speak, of thousands of short-range diversifications producing separate species. Some of the peculiarities of these separate species are due to non-selective accidents; but all the rest have been closely guided and moulded by natural selection.

Darwin introduced time into biology, and forced us to regard human history as the extension of a general process of change, operating by an automatic natural mechanism. Darwinism to-day has fully confirmed these general conclusions, but has, in addition, enabled us to distinguish between different types of change, and to link up human with biological history more fruitfully by introducing the idea of progress and the criterion of desirable or undesirable evolutionary direction.

The modern extension of Darwinism has also enabled us to analyse the process of selection in a way that was impossible in Darwin's day. In the first place, the intensity of selection may vary very considerably, and this will be reflected in its results. Where a group is freed from the full normal pressure of competitors or enemies, it is enabled to evolve in quite unusual directions. The classical examples of this are found on remote oceanic islands. In such areas of biological low pressure, the few types which manage to find their way thither proceed to radiate out in many new directions. The best instance is that of the birds called sickle-bills (*Drepanididae*) on the Hawaiian archipelago. Derived from some kind of honey-creeper, they have in their oceanic isolation evolved into no less than 18 separate genera, adapted to an extraordinary range of habits, from nut- to insect-eaters, from woodpecker-like types to nectar-sippers, each with a characteristic form of bill.

In the Great Lakes of Africa, nature has conducted a demonstrative experiment by permitting powerful predatory fish to reach some lakes but not others. The little fish known as Cichlids exist in all the lakes. Where predators are present, as in Lake Albert, only four different Cichlid species have evolved since the Ice Age; but where predators are absent, as in Lake Victoria, there are over fifty Cichlid species, adapted to many new habitats and ways of life. Predator-pressure has had a restrictive effect on the diversification of prey.

The same sort of thing has happened in Australia, where the early or marsupial type of mammal was isolated before the more efficient placental type had been evolved. Accordingly, as everyone knows, the marsupials in Australia have produced dozens of types, such as kangaroos, Tasmanian wolf, and flying phalanger, not found either living or fossil in any other part of the world. Elsewhere the pressure of more efficient competitors has prevented this efflorescence, and only a few generalized marsupials, such as the American opossum, have survived.

The Australian marsupials illustrate another point. The Australian area is much smaller and less varied than the great land masses of the northern hemisphere where the higher placentals evolved. There is less scope for variation, less need for extremes of efficiency, so that general selection-pressure never became so intense. As a result, the Australian marsupials were not pushed so hard or so far along their lines of

specialization as were the placentals; they were not forced
to such a pitch either of biomechanical efficiency or of
intelligence; and they at once go downhill and are threatened
with extinction when they have to compete with introduced
placental types.

Even more interesting are the recent studies on qualitative
differences in the results of different kinds of selection, or,
if you prefer, of selection operating in different circumstances. Thus a peculiarly acute competition takes place
before birth among such mammals as produce several young
at a time. More eggs are always fertilized than can survive
to birth; there is thus an intra-uterine selection which puts
a premium on quick and vigorous growth, for any laggard
embryos will fail to get their fair share of the available
nutriment and will die and be resorbed or aborted. As J.
B. S. Haldane has pointed out, this pre-natal rapidity of
growth will certainly tend to continue after birth; and so the
slow growth and prolonged infancy which makes human
learning possible could never have been evolved except
in a mammalian stock like that of the monkeys, where only
one young is normally born at a time.

Haldane has also drawn attention to the interesting point
that instinctive altruism, such as is shown by bees or ants,
cannot possibly be evolved except in social organisms where
reproduction is confined to a limited caste and the altruistic
types are sterile.

The most far-reaching conclusion deriving from modern
analysis, however, is that the results of natural selection are
not necessarily beneficial to the species, and may even be
harmful. This apparent paradox is based on the fact that
much of the struggle for existence is not directed against the
forces of nature, nor against enemies, nor against competitors
of other species, but against other members of the same
species. Not only does the species as a whole have to struggle
(in a metaphorical sense) to survive and reproduce, but so
do the individuals within it. In a given species of butterfly, for example, only a small proportion of the young caterpillars will survive into the butterfly stage. But among these,

the decision as to which shall reproduce may depend on whether one can escape detection by its enemies better than others. Accordingly protective resemblance, as, for instance, of the famous Kallima to a dead leaf complete with imitation veins and mould-spots, may be pushed to an incredibly high pitch, and yet have no effect on the survival of the species as a whole, which will be decided mainly by the capacity of the caterpillars to survive their much more numerous dangers.

Other examples of such "hypertelic" adaptations are seen in the leaf-fish, which drifts up to within reach of its prey under the guise of a floating dead leaf; the sea-horse of the Sargasso Sea, which resembles a bit of Sargasso weed; or the extraordinary plant-bug *Heteronotus*, which carries about an imitation ant on its upper surface to scare off its enemies.

This *intra-specific* competition is most obvious when rival males compete for mates, and most acute when polygamy prevails and success in reproduction thus brings a multiple advantage. When this is so, the characters which bring success in mating may become so over-developed as to embarrass their possessors in the struggle for mere existence, as with the train of the peacock or the wings—almost useless for flight—of the argus pheasant. Sexual selection here has benefited none but certain types of males as against others: its results for the species as a whole are harmful.

This distinction, it is clear, has great importance for human affairs. Apologists for the *laisser-faire* system on the one hand and for militarism on the other hand, appealed to the Darwinian struggle for existence as a justification. Now we realize that these forms of the struggle, far from being helpful, are either useless, in which case they will be also wasteful, or actually inimical to progress.

Space forbids more than the barest mention of the ways in which studies on development have illuminated some of the dark places of evolution. I will confine myself to two examples. The antlers of a stag, like the jaws of a male stag-beetle and many other masculine characteristics, increase

disproportionately with the increase in the adult size of the
animal. In a small stag, the antlers average about 2 per cent.
of his total weight. But in a large stag weighing as much,
the antlers average almost 4 per cent.—while the body has
doubled its weight, they have quadrupled theirs.

If now during the evolution of deer, selection takes place
for increased bulk, there will be an automatic tendency for
the antlers to increase in relative size (a conclusion borne
out in general by the relative weight of antlers in species of
deer of different sizes). Selection may also operate directly
on antler-size, but so far as our automatic tendency is
operative, change in relative antler-size is a mere by-product
of change in general size. It is what Darwin called a "correlated character"—something useless in itself but correlated
with some other character which is useful. We now know of
a great many such correlated characters—for instance, tun-
ing up or down the activity of one or other of the ductless
glands to adjust the animal to its particular environment
may produce changes in colour or in bodily proportions—
and without question a great many apparently meaningless
differences characterizing related species or sub-species
are mere external signs of such invisible but insignificant
inner adaptations.

Another old objection to Darwinian explanations of evolution is the incredible complexity of the detailed adjustments needed to effect a change such as the lengthening of
an animal's neck. To take but this one example: all the
tendons tying the neck vertebrae together must be strengthened and their direction adjusted. How could random
variation and selection account for this? We now know that
the tissue of which tendons are made, like many other
tissues of the body, has the faculty of responding to demands
upon it—by excess growth and by changes in the direction
of its fibres. Granted this one basic adaptation, all the rest
follow. The myriad detailed adjustments are not determined
by heredity and selection, but are built anew in each individual during its development.

In these and many other ways our modern knowledge of

growth and development has lightened the burden on natural selection, at the same time that advances in heredity have shown natural selection to be a much more flexible instrument than the last generation of biologists thought possible.

To sum up, Darwinism to-day is very much alive. In certain respects, indeed, modern evolutionary theory is more Darwinian than Darwin was himself. Darwin's special contribution to the evolution problem was the theory of natural selection, but, owing to the rudimentary state of knowledge in certain biological fields, he was forced to bolster this up with subsidiary Lamarckian hypotheses, of the inheritance of the effects of use and disuse and of modifications produced by the direct agency of the environment. To-day we are able to reject these subsidiary hypotheses, and can demonstrate that naural selection is omnipresent and virtually the only guiding agency in evolution.

Darwin has with some justice been called the Newton of biology. Like Newton, he gave his science a unifying concept, and one capable of extension into every corner of its field. There are evolutionary implications in every branch of biology. The human physiologist may provide the most detailed physico-chemical analysis of some bodily process: but his description will be incomplete unless he takes account of its evolutionary history as well.

The unifying power of the concept is also seen in the way in which the study of evolution makes a call upon the most diverse fields of biological study and links them together in solving its problems. Comparative anatomy, embryology, natural history and ecology, classification, palaeontology, genetics and cytology, the study of behaviour—all these and many more are now meeting and illuminating each other in the new evolutionary synthesis.

Evolution, too, was one of the first branches of inquiry to demand that relativist point of view which is becoming increasingly central to the modern scientific outlook. The single organism, looked at through evolutionary spectacles, has no meaning except in relation to a particular environment, to a particular set of enemies and competitors, to a particular past history, and to a particular set of potentialities for the future. All this was implicit in Darwin's masterly formulation of the problem.

The implications for man and for his general conception of nature and of his own place in nature are equally far-reaching. The idea of a past Golden Age vanished into smoke; so did all static conceptions of human life. In their place we see inevitable change and possible progress, while at the same time the time-span of the human drama is enlarged a thousand-fold in the past and still more in the future.

Newton showed that the same general principles applied to the motion of heavenly bodies and to that of the humblest terrestrial objects. Similarly, Darwin, with his few simple principles of the struggle for existence, natural selection, and consequent adaptation, linked man with all the rest of life, from monkeys and flowers to bacteria and amoebae, in a common web of necessity and change. The fundamental principles of Newtonian physics have now been superseded (though it still remains as the most effective first approximation to physical truth). Though Darwin's principles have been more modified in detail than Newton's, there seems less likelihood of their being superseded by a different set of basic principles. There are no signs that evolutionary biology will not indefinitely remain Darwinian.

THOMAS HENRY HUXLEY AND JULIAN HUXLEY: AN IMAGINARY INTERVIEW[1]

JULIAN (*rather crossly*): The fellow who runs these interviews has told me to come here and exchange a few words with my grandfather, Thomas Henry Huxley, who died in 1895 at the beginning of his seventy-first year. That's all very well, but how can even the B.B.C. put one in touch with a world of departed spirits—in the existence of which my grandfather no more believed than I do, though he was scrupulously undogmatic in all merely speculative judgments of that kind?

I remember him very vividly, as a child does.

THOMAS HENRY: And I remember you, young Julian.

JULIAN: But what *are* you?

THOMAS HENRY: A projection of your private fancy.

JULIAN: That's a good working hypothesis, anyhow. After all, your achievements, both as a scientist and as an expositor of science, have meant a tremendous lot to me, and did exercise a most powerful influence on my early life and career.

THOMAS HENRY: Well, there's no reason why our working hypothesis should obstruct our conversation. You spoke of your career, Julian. I understand that you have become a biologist, like myself. I knew you had the makings of a biologist in you, my boy, from the day that you, as a child of seven, put me right on a point of biological fact.

JULIAN: My father often told me about that. I wish I could remember the occasion!

THOMAS HENRY: Yes. It was at the luncheon-table. There was some talk about parental care in animals, and I remarked that one didn't find it among fish. Whereupon you piped up: "What about the stickleback, Gran'pater?" How we all laughed!

[1] Originally arranged as a broadcast.

JULIAN: I bet you did.

THOMAS HENRY: The beauty of it was that you were right. My general statement—that fishes take no care of their young—was true. But of course there are sporadic exceptions. And the stickleback is one of them.

JULIAN (*laughing*): Well, it's very gratifying. I think I'd been reading one of those popular children's books on biology by Arabella Buckley.

THOMAS HENRY: I fancy you had. . . . Ah, those were happy times—or so we thought. In any case, they were very happy in comparison with your present chaos.

JULIAN: I gather you don't find 1942 a very congenial period? I'm not surprised!

THOMAS HENRY: From all I hear, it's a bad time for a Victorian scientist to come visiting.

JULIAN: You discussed a great many topics in those famous essays of yours, but I don't remember that war was among them.

THOMAS HENRY: I think you are right. We lived through various wars: but we never conceived, even as an idle speculation, that the world as a whole would ever again collapse into a state of belligerent barbarism, nor did we dream of what you call total war.

JULIAN: And what about the political theories of to-day? You, I know, like most progressive men of your time, were a great admirer of German science, German literature, German philosophy. What do you make of their modern doctrines of Blood and Soil, of Aryan and Nordic racial superiority, of their burning of books, their persecution of thought because it is unorthodox by Nazi standards, or even because it is Jewish?

THOMAS HENRY: It appals me. Knowing that cranks are always with us, I'm not in the least surprised to find *some* people believing such nonsense. But that it can have become the official doctrine of a great nation, and apparently one of the forces contributing to its military triumphs, and to its belief in its high destiny—this I find scarcely conceivable.

JULIAN: It isn't conceivable—but it's happened.

THOMAS HENRY: It must have shaken the very foundations of your thinking.

JULIAN: Of course, we have had nearly thirty years to adjust ourselves to the collapse of the world system that seemed so stable and so full of promise in your time and even in my young days. . . . First the war of 1914-18; then a period of cynical disillusionment; then the most spectacular economic collapse in history; then the rise of Fascist aggression. But there are plenty of people who have still not adjusted themselves, and quite fail to realize that they're living in the middle of one of the greatest revolutions in human history.

THOMAS HENRY: What about those who *do* realize that they are living in a revolution, but happen not to enjoy the fact? I am trying, you see, to visualize the impact of the situation.

JULIAN: Well, there are several ways in which such people react. A few indulge in tempered optimism and try to plan ahead for the new world that must some time or other emerge. Some—and these perhaps the majority—are consciously pessimistic. And many try to escape from an unacknowledged pessimism by taking refuge in superstitions, like astrology, or in mere hedonism.

I expect this widespread pessimism strikes you as one of the chief differences between our age and yours.

THOMAS HENRY: I always did my best to demonstrate the falsity of unreasoning optimism, about the inevitability of progress and the like. But it is true that the general background of our age was optimistic; knowledge and invention and material wealth were all increasing; and superstition and bigotry were being pushed on to the defensive. Optimism, within limits, seemed justifiable.

JULIAN: Actually you were very lucky in your period. It seems to us to-day that you had a double advantage. New discovery and new techniques, in making expansion inevitable, had rendered hope reasonable, while at the same time the stable framework provided by traditional ways of thinking had not yet been lost.

THOMAS HENRY: I'm not sure that I understand you. I would say that we *had* largely destroyed traditional ways of thinking—at any rate, the claims of theological orthodoxy and of out-of-date authoritarian systems of political thought.

JUILAN: Yes. But you still lived in a tidy world of absolute Truth and absolute Morality.

THOMAS HENRY: Can you really say that? We believed in the scientific spirit and therefore in a steadily increasing harvest of truth and a steady destruction of error. And we believed that the laws of moral conduct resemble the laws of nature in being discoverable only by observation and experiment. But we emphatically repudiated the claims of the clerics and all others who set themselves up to be in possession of a complete body of truth and a complete system of morals.

JULIAN: All the same, though you did attack and overthrow authoritarian truth and authoritarian morals, the truth and the morality which you were discovering and testing were still surely regarded as absolutes. To-day the more philosophical among us prefer to regard science and morality from a relative point of view, as organs of society, varying according to the conditions of the time.

THOMAS HENRY: But surely you would not deny that morality has an absolute quality—what Kant called the Categorical Imperative?

JULIAN: It has the quality of being *felt* as absolute. But that, according to modern psychological discoveries, is the result of the somewhat crude psychological process called repression, which we all undergo in infancy.

THOMAS HENRY: I should like to know rather more about these discoveries you talk of before committing myself to what seems at first hearing to be a deplorable degree of moral relativity.

JULIAN: I would recommend your perusing some of the works of Freud. You will undoubtedly experience a considerable inner resistance against accepting his main conclusions, just as many in your time experienced a resistance against accepting the conclusions of Darwin. But once that resist-

ance is overcome, I venture to say that you will find them
very illuminating.

THOMAS HENRY: I hope so. But I still fail to see how they
can dethrone morality from its position of transcendental
importance in life.

JULIAN: That, if I may say so, is because you were always
a great moralist as well as a great scientist. But there's a
question which I have longed to ask you ever since, as a
young man, I read your famous Romanes lecture, *Evolution
and Ethics.* There you stated (I remember the passage
vividly) that the ethical progress of society depends not on
imitating the cosmic process but in combating it, and by
the cosmic process you of course meant mainly the ruthless
struggle for existence. As an evolutionist, I never understood
how man, himself a part of nature, could fulfil his destiny
by fighting against that same process which gave him birth.

THOMAS HENRY: Is it not self-evident? Any theory of
ethics cannot but repudiate the gladiatorial theory of life;
the practice of virtue must be opposed to the type of conduct which is successful in the cosmic struggle for existence.

JULIAN: I begin to see your point. But I think that
modern biology has something rather different to say on the
subject. To-day, after eighty years, we look back to Darwin
as the Newton of our science, the man who gave it the unifying concept for which it had been waiting. . . .

THOMAS HENRY (*interrupting*): Yes, yes, very true.
That was how his work seemed at the time—a flash of light
illuminating a dark and confused landscape. When I first
read *The Origin of Species*, I said to myself, "How extremely
stupid not to have thought of that!"

JULIAN: Yes, I remember. And you had the rare privilege
for a scientist, not only of living through one of the great
controversies of science, but of playing an outstanding part
in getting the new theory accepted. But to return to my
point. In your day, the urgency was to demonstrate the
fact of evolution. But now biology has moved beyond that
stage and has built up a fairly full and detailed picture
both of the course of evolution and of its methods.

THOMAS HENRY: The theory of Natural Selection as Darwin presented it was certainly very general, and I confess that I was always a little sceptical over the theorizing zeal of some of his followers, and anxious for a fuller basis of concrete fact. So do tell me something about the new developments.

JULIAN: Well, for one thing we now have a pretty thorough knowledge of the astonishingly elaborate machinery of heredity and hereditary change through which evolution comes into being. But it would take too long to go into all that now, and I can only recommend that you include some books on mendelian genetics in your reading list. What I think is chiefly relevant to our discussion is that biologists have now arrived at two far-reaching conclusions: one about the struggle for existence, the other about its results.

THOMAS HENRY (reminiscently): The struggle for existence—my friend Tennyson summed it up: "Nature red in tooth and claw."

JULIAN: That appears to have been an undue simplification. For instance, intelligence seems to have played as important a part in evolution as brute force, and co-operation has contributed as much as competition.

THOMAS HENRY: That certainly bears thinking about.

JULIAN: But that is not my main point. We now distinguish two radically different forms of the struggle for existence. One is primarily a struggle of the species as a whole against its enemies and against the adverse forces of nature, and the other is a struggle for success between individual members of the species. And this latter kind of competition within the species may not benefit or improve the species as a whole in any way, and in some cases can be shown to be actually harmful to it.

THOMAS HENRY: That seems a paradox, but nature is often paradoxical, and I am prepared to accept it. You imply that my "cosmic process" represents only this less useful form of the struggle, while the ethical force which makes for human progress represents the other?

JULIAN: Roughly speaking, yes. And your word *progress* brings me to my second point. I think the most important outcome of biology for general thought has been the demonstration that there *is* such a thing as progress in biological evolution.

THOMAS HENRY: You mean even apart from man? But there is the fact of degeneration to reckon with, and also the fact that an amoeba or a louse is every whit as well adapted to survive as a singing bird or the most gifted human being.

JULIAN: But surely progress does not cease to exist either because it is not universal or because it is not inevitable? Your generation put evolution on the map: ours has mapped evolution. And our analysis has shown that progress is one of the types of evolutionary change. It is true that most of the results of evolution are not progressive. Much is mere change; much else, though advance, is one-sided advance, doomed to come eventually to a dead end. But a narrow thread of true progress does run through the whole web of change.

THOMAS HENRY: I hope you are not arguing in a circle, and defining progress merely from a human standpoint. After all, man is but one species among hundreds of thousands.

JULIAN: No, progress can be defined biologically in a perfectly objective way, as denoting increased harmony of construction, increased capacity for knowledge and for feeling, and increased control over nature, increased independence of outer change.

THOMAS HENRY: I still have the feeling that you are slipping back into an anthropomorphic view, and creating progress in your own image.

JULIAN: I don't think so. In fact, it is the exact reverse. The Middle Ages judged the universe from the standpoint of man: the modern biologist investigates the trends of evolution, and then finds that man happens to be at the top of the trend toward progress.

THOMAS HENRY: Man as the trustee of progress instead of the Lord of Creation?

JULIAN: If you like. At any rate, it is some comfort to feel that there is some standard, some direction in things, quite independent of ourselves. Against that background, this fearful war can be seen in better proportion and better perspective, and our efforts and sufferings appear as part of a process which extends far beyond the immediate necessity of winning.

THOMAS HENRY: That is one of the gifts of science: it sets our life in the midst of spacious and inspiring vistas, while never allowing us the delusion that we can achieve anything without effort. But ultimate standards are rather too large a proposition to discuss now: it's time for me to leave you.

JULIAN: Not so soon, surely?

THOMAS HENRY: What can it matter? I am merely, after all, a projection of your private fancy. Wasn't that agreed at the outset?

JULIAN: All the same, there's much else we could say to each other.

THOMAS HENRY: Indeed, yes. Even from the little you've had time to tell me, it's clear that science has made great strides since my day. I am old, I come from another age, but perhaps I am not entirely out of date.

JULIAN: No, you're certainly not.

THOMAS HENRY: If I may bring a message from my age to yours, I would say three things. First, do not let the advance of science slacken, for knowledge is power, and the pursuit of truth is one of the ultimate and eternal imperatives for man. Second, do not allow science to be divorced from morality: your age has different views on morality from mine, but we both agree that moral rectitude is another of the ultimate human imperatives, and that it is linked with something outside ourselves. Finally, there is freedom: one of the sentences I am proud to have written is this—"It is better for a man to go wrong in freedom than to go right in chains." Therefore I say to you: Hold fast to truth, to justice, and to freedom. These are still the only foundations on which any enduring new world can be built.

DOCTOR SPOONER: THE GROWTH
OF A LEGEND

DOCTOR SPOONER was one of the rare few who have not only become a legend during their lifetime, but, like Colonel Boycott, given their name to a new word. The word "Spoonerism" appeared in our dictionaries years before Spooner's death. A Spoonerism is defined—I quote the big Oxford Dictionary—as "an accidental transposition of the initial sounds, or other parts, of two or more words." The example given in the Concise Oxford Dictionary is "a well-boiled icicle" instead of "a well-oiled bicycle"—to my mind, a very poor one, but I hope to give plenty of better ones later.

Almost all of us make Spoonerisms sometimes, and some people deliberately invent them. Why, then, has Spooner's name been attached to this verbal form of slip? And why have so many Spoonerisms been quite unjustly fastened on to him as their parent? The growth of a legend such as this is quite an interesting subject for study, and I shall discuss the Spoonerism from this angle. I had the good fortune to serve under Doctor Spooner for six years when I was a Fellow of New College and he was Warden of that ancient and distinguished foundation. He established what must, I think, be a record for an Oxford or Cambridge college, namely continuous residence for sixty-three years without missing a single term—first as undergraduate, then as Fellow and Tutor, then Dean, and eventually Warden. And he survived and remained active for several years after his retirement at the age of eighty.

Though he published very little, he was a good scholar and a good teacher. He was an excellent administrator, with the rare gift of making people feel that he was deeply interested in their own particular affairs. He worked very hard, without any thought of self, and gave the impression of possessing that rare quality which I can only describe as saintliness. But he had his peculiarities. To begin with, he was an albino—not a full albino with pink eyes, but one with very pale blue eyes and white hair just tinged with straw-colour. As is common with albinos, he was very short-sighted and used to read with his eyes within a couple of inches of the paper. When, at the age of thirteen, I went up to stand for a scholarship at Eton, he was the examiner, and I shall never forget seeing him reading our exam papers in this fashion, every now and then putting the paper down on the desk and making a big mark with a big blue pencil on some mistake—every time this happened I would always imagine that it was my paper he was dealing with. Then he was rather a small man with a strange, rather butterfly sort of quality in his voice. And finally, he did say, and write, and do some very odd things. A neurologist would doubt-less tell us that he had something a little wrong with some of the association centres in his brain, which led to his saying the wrong word, or in some way making the wrong association. The curious thing was that this did not make him any the less efficient in the varied intricacies of college business.

True Spoonerisms, in the dictionary sense, he very rarely produced. There is, however, a good deal of evidence for his having actually announced the hymn "Conquering Kings their titles take . . ." as "Kinkering Congs." And for his having said to a stranger who was sitting in his seat in chapel: "Excuse me, but I think you are occupewing my pie." But almost all the old favourites among Spoonerisms are pure inventions, which were afterwards tacked on to him. For instance, he never really said to the lady who asked him what happened to the cat which fell from a fourth-story window: "Oh, she just popped on her drawers and away she went." Nor did he ever say to the lazy undergraduate: "You have hissed all my mystery lectures. In fact, you have tasted two whole worms and you must leave Oxford this afternoon by the Town Drain." As I said, most of his actual slips were in the nature of what one might call "paraphrasia."

I twice personally heard him make a slip of this sort. When the Oxford University Expedition was going to Spitsbergen, I had been explaining to him that the reason for our choice of that barren land was that, owing to the Gulf Stream, you could go so far north without great difficulty. When I called to say good-bye, he retailed this to his wife: "My dear, Mr. Huxley assures me that it's no farther from the north coast of Spitsbergen to the North Pole than it is from Land's End to John of Gaunt!" That was a typical false association. Again, once when I was going with him on some matter of college business to a village near Oxford, we passed a farm which I happened to know was called Bayswater Farm. And as we passed this he turned to me and, with his customary sweet smile said: "A curious thing, my dear Huxley, but that farm's called Piccadilly." My only conclusion was that both Piccadilly and Bayswater are in the West End of London.

Then there is another one that I believe to be well authenticated. A Fellow of the college had been ill, and in his absence a piece of college business had been decided, in a way which went against his known views; a day or so later, Spooner, meeting the man's wife in the street, asked after his health and then said: "But I'm afraid that when he hears what we did at the college meeting yesterday he'll gnash his tail!" That, I think, bears the stamp of truth. Then a very curious one, which a friend assures me actually happened. The Indian mystic, Krishnamurti, was, if you remember, taken up as a young man by Mrs. Annie Besant, who expressed the view that he was an incarnation of Jesus. He came up for admission as an undergraduate at New College. As the lists were being gone through, the Warden said: "Next we come to the name of Mr. Krishnamurti. I understand that Mr. Krishnamurti is supposed to be an incarnation of Our Lord, so of course we can't have him at New College." I think we all see what he meant, but he certainly put it in a rather curious way. As illustrating the way legends grow, that story afterwards had another—quite mythical one—tacked on to it, to the effect that Spooner added that he might have a better chance if he tried a certain other college, the President of which notoriously had a weakness for celebrities.

Then there is a story which I don't vouch for, though it rings true to type. Spooner was supposed to have been preaching one day in a village which was one of the New College livings, and gave a long sermon all about Aristotle. There were only about two people in the congregation who had ever heard of Aristotle, and their rather dim recollections didn't tally very well with what the Warden had been saying. He had finished his sermon and was half-way down the pulpit stairs when suddenly something struck him, and he trotted up again and said: "Excuse me, dear brethren: I just want to say that in my sermon, wherever I said Aristotle I *should* have said St. Paul."

Then it is not generally known that he sometimes did the same sort of thing—committing what I called "paraphrasia" —in writing as well as in speaking. I once had a pupil— let us for the sake of argument say his name was Wilson— who, after he'd taken his degree, wrote to the Warden asking if he could stay up for a year, as he wanted to continue working under his tutor—in other words, me. He showed me the letter he received in reply. It began: "My dear Wilford"—his name being Wilson—"I think it would be a very good thing if you stayed up and went on working under your father." Here he had not noticed what he had done. But apparently he used sometimes to read over his letters and see that he had made a mistake. If so, he used to scratch out the mistake—but just with one line, so that you could still read the wrong word—and write the right word over the top. I was shown two letters of this sort by a tutor of New College. One of them was rather pathetic. It ended up "Yours very truly," but underneath, with a line through it, "poorly." I suppose he was feeling poorly when he wrote the letter. Another was written to congratulate the same man on his wife's recovery from a serious illness. In it he wrote: "I am so glad to hear that you are at least relieved from your terrible burden of anxiety," and underneath, with a line through it, "debt"—an all too normal association!

Then he sometimes used to make slips in action. The wife of an Oxford Professor once told me that she had been dining at New College in the Warden's lodgings, where there is a very fine but very slippery old oak staircase you have to go down from the drawing-room. When she was going home the Warden said: "Oh, I'll come and turn on the other lights and see you safely down the stairs." But when he got to the staircase he turned out the only light that was on, and proceeded to lead the way down in total darkness. Luckily his daughter came to the rescue and switched the lights on.

With all these peculiarities, it was little wonder that the legend grew. Let us remember that legends grow very readily in old-fashioned University circles, especially if aided by the inventions of rather naughty colleagues. Anyhow, this certainly happened in New College in the 'seventies and 'eighties—with the result that the word Spoonerism—I cite the large Oxford Dictionary—"was in colloquial use in Oxford as early as 1885 and in general use all over the country before 1900."

By now, there are hundreds of these invented stories fastened on to the legend of Spooner—mostly silly, but some of them, I really think, have enriched our national stock of humour. Let me emphasize again that all these are quite certainly mythical. There is a familiar one which I like very much about his having (so the story ran) made an engagement to meet a man at a certain public-house in south London. He came back very, very tired and weary at the end of the day, without having been able to find the man; but it turned out the public-house that he had been vaguely looking for was the Dull Man, Greenwich, whereas really the appointment was for the Green Man, Dulwich.

Perhaps the best of all Spoonerisms are the very simple ones; the one I think I personally like best is the tale—again quite mythical—of Spooner having his hat blown off and running after it, saying, "Oh please, will nobody pat my

hiccup." But there is a very elaborate and ridiculous one
that I rather enjoy. He and Mrs. Spooner—so the story
goes—were taking a vacation in Switzerland, where he got
interested in glaciers and had been studying books on the
subject till he was full of technical terms like crevasses, and
erratic blocks, and moraines, and seracs, and all the rest of
it. And then one day he had gone out for a long walk with
his wife, who, by the way, was a handsome woman, considerably bigger than he was, and they hadn't come back
for lunch. People were getting anxious, when at last he
turned up. Asked what had happened, he said: "Oh, we had
a very remarkable experience. We went far up the valley,
right out of sight of the hotel, and as we turned a corner,
we found ourselves completely surrounded by erotic blacks."
He meant, of course, erratic blocks—the big boulders left
standing about after being transported by an ice-sheet.

Then there is one so obviously made up that I need not
labour the fact. It is also so subtle, or perhaps I should say
so improbable, that many people don't think it funny at all.
The story was that he went into an optician's shop in Oxford
and asked for a signifying glass. The optician said: "Excuse
me, I didn't quite understand?" "Oh, just an ordinary signifying glass." "I'm afraid we don't stock them: could we write
to London for one?" "Oh, no, it doesn't magnify, it doesn't
magnify" . . .

The legend grew in other ways too. I remember the story
of a Scotsman being shown round Oxford by a don friend
of his. He was always asking what everything cost and what
such-and-such a position was worth. He having thus discovered the salaries of the Master of Balliol, the Rector of
Exeter, the Dean of Christchurch, the Warden of Wadham,
and so on, his friend saw Spooner and pointed him out—
this was in the days before he became Warden—and said:
"Look, there goes the albino of New College." "Very interesting," said the Scot; "and what may the Albinoship of
New College be wor-rth?"

Spooner naturally knew of his reputation, though apparently he was not conscious of any of his actual lapses at the

time that he made them. I think perhaps the greatest applause he ever got was once at a college Gaudy, when past members of the college come up for a reunion. He concluded one of his charming little speeches with the words: "And now I suppose I'd better sit down, or I might be saying—er—one of those things."

To wind up, I will tell one of his real utterances which I had direct from a distinguished historian who overheard it. Spooner after his retirement—though retired, of course he was still called Warden by everybody—had invited to some New College celebration the Head of another college where the title of the Head is *President*. The President was late—and everybody was waiting rather impatiently. At last in he came. Spooner was standing with his back to the door, and the President strode up to him, clapped him on the shoulder and stretched out his hand. You or I would have said "Good evening, President," or "It's all right," or something like that, but what Dr. Spooner did actually say was "Good-bye, Warden." That illustrates very well the strange little kink which he had in his brain—which yet did not prevent him being an extremely efficient and extremely charming man. Good-bye Warden—I'll close on that: good-bye to a man I am happy to have served under, a man who was the direct or indirect cause of a considerable addition to the world's stock of good-natured laughter: a man who became a legend in his own lifetime, and supported that somewhat embarrassing position with dignity and charm. So—good-bye, Warden!

BIRDS AND MEN ON ST. KILDA

REMOTE islands have a fascination for the biologist. Their inaccessibility makes them a sanctuary, both for rare species and for immense congregations of commoner ones. Their isolation has prevented many forms from reaching them at all, so that what they lack is as interesting as what they possess. And this same isolation, combined with the difference of conditions, has often encouraged the evolution of special local types.

St. Kilda has all these biological attractions. It is scientifically celebrated as the home of the St. Kilda wren, a sub-species of the common wren so distinct that it was for some time classified as a separate species. It is one of the few places in Britain where Leach's fork-tailed petrel nests —a beautiful little creature still more martin-like than its common relative the storm petrel. On one of its three main component islands there lives over a fifth of the world's entire stock of gannets—those most spectacular of all our sea-birds; while a conservative estimate of its puffin population would be a quarter of a million. It has a melancholy historical attraction as the site of the last recorded British occurrence of the great auk. In 1821, only twenty-three years before the final extinction of the species, a specimen was captured there on a ledge of cliff. It eventually passed into the hands of John Fleming, who kept it alive for some time on the vessel of the Northern Lighthouse Commissioners. Unfortunately, when they reached the Clyde, the bird escaped while being indulged with a swim in the sea, contriving to slip the cord attached to one leg.

St. Kilda also forms a part of a region where evolution can be studied in action. All round the north-west and north of Scotland, the islands harbour animals and plants which are slightly different from those of the mainland. To take but a few examples from birds, the Shetland wren is also

distinct enough to be classified as a distinct sub-species. So
is the Shetland starling, and the hedge-sparrow and the song-
thrush from the Hebrides.

What is more, the distinctive types of the Scottish islands
form part of a graded system, a field of change, which
extends inwards to the mainland coasts and outwards to the
Faeroes and Iceland. If you take measurements of the different local races of wrens, you find that they increase in
size at a pretty definite rate with increasing north latitude—
almost 1½ per cent. increase in size for every degree. The
blackbirds of the western Highlands appear to differ slightly
from those of Britain as a whole, and the difference is in the
direction of that seen in the more distinctive race of the
Hebrides.

We cannot suppose that wrens and thrushes were able to
support glacial conditions: so that the observed changes
must have taken place since the end of the Ice Age, certainly
less than 15,000 years ago—an infinitesimal period in the
thousand-million-year perspective of evolution.

There is no necessity for the British biologist to go to the
high arctic or to the tropics to study evolution: he has problems of the greatest interest on the doorstep of his own
country.

So it came about that, looking for a holiday with a point
to it, I attached myself this spring to an ornithological party
which was going to visit St. Kilda and other normally
unvisited Scottish islands.

St. Kilda was unquestionably the high spot of the voyage,
not merely because of its biological interest but for its
astonishing scenery and its human history. It is forty miles
to westward of the Outer Hebrides. Forty miles doesn't
sound far; but it is a good way for a 25-ton yacht against the
wind, and we were all night making the island after leaving
the Sound of Harris. The one anchorage is Village Bay in
the island of Hirta, and even that is unsafe with southerly or
easterly winds. The first sight of this island is a little dis-
appointing—a grassy coomb, a little like the head of Fair-
field in the English Lakes, with the deserted village in its

centre. After breakfast, we set off up to Conachair, the highest point, strung out in a line so as to cover more ground, as we wanted to make a survey of all the land birds —a survey later published in *British Birds* by Max Nicholson and James Fisher. An extraordinary fact was the number of snipe in and around the old village, although it did not look at all like snipe country.

Another peculiarity of St. Kilda is that the rock pipit, which is usually confined to a narrow zone along the sea cliffs, here extends far inland, into regions which would normally be the preserve of its relative the meadow pipit— and this in spite of the fact that meadow pipits also breed on the island.

This phenomenon, of changed habits toward the limits of the range of a species, or in other exceptional conditions, we encountered in several other birds elsewhere. The reed bunting of Lewis and the mainland opposite, in the absence of their usual sallow thickets and reed-beds, were nesting on islets in lochs, where, owing to the absence of browsing sheep, there were rather more trees and shrubs than on the mainland. Herons nest here in very small colonies, often on the face of a cliff, the nests sometimes resting on the ground. On an island in a loch on the east of Harris, some of the birds in a herring gull colony had made their nests among the roots of small trees—an astonishing situation for a gull.

Also on this islet was a reed bunting whose song differed so much from the normal type of the species that we were at first completely puzzled as to what the bird might be. But that is another story. The change of song that you find in many birds in the north is part of the general field of change in the region. The Shetland wren combines a distinctive rhythm and stridency of song with its larger size and darker plumage: the blackbirds of the north-west, though almost undistinguishable in appearance, have a feebler, less mellow song, more thrush-like in quality than their southern relatives.

Many plants, too, show changed habits in these parts. A cliff heronry we visited was in the midst of a sheet of blue-bells running up into the heather. Bluebells grow in the

open all along our western coasts, from the Scillies to Cape
Wrath. It must be the lesser rainfall inland and to the east
which there restricts them to woodland.

All over the western Highlands the spotted orchis, instead
of growing in the sheltered and rather rich situations where
southerners expect to find it, invades the moor and grows
even among the heather. It was growing all over the bare
slopes of St. Kilda.

Finally there were the primroses. Though it was June,
they were in full bloom on St. Kilda wherever there was a
moist sheltered place. They were all down the gullies of the
southern cliff; one of the most unexpected items of natural
history that I ever saw or am likely to see was a fulmar
petrel sitting on its nest at over 1300 feet on the cliffs of
Conachair, entirely surrounded by large primroses!

The primroses have brought me to the cliffs. These are
quite astonishing. Those of Hirta are the highest in Britain,
within a yard or so of 1400 feet. They are not, however,
nearly so precipitous as those of Foula in the Shetland or
Hoy in Orkney. They break down to the sea in steep green
steps, interrupted by sheerer clifflets of bare rock. The entire
slope is dotted with white specks. The impression is of
strange cliff flowers; but they are in reality fulmar petrels,
many thousands in sight at once.

Across the sea, four miles away, is Boreray, the home of
the gannets. It lies there, a green uprising wedge, with two
fine stacks off its western face; through the glasses these are
seen to be topped with creamy white—dense crowds of
breeding gannets. Seen thus from a distance it looks romantic enough, but the closer view is staggering. I have been in
a good many parts of the world; but I can only recall two
places which beat Boreray in immediate spectacular quality
—the Grand Canyon and the Virunga volcanoes in the
Western African Rift.

We sailed there in the afternoon. Landing is nowhere
easy, but least difficult on the rocks at the foot of a steep grass
slope. I measured the angle of slope on the six-inch map and
found it exactly $45°$— 1 in $\sqrt{2}$. To those who climb it on

a hot June day it looks and feels like 60°. It is honey-combed with puffin burrows; we estimated that over 50,000 puffins were nesting in it. Some members of Lord Dumfrie's party on Hirta had come with us to try to secure fresh meat in the shape of the sheep which run wild on Boreray. At the sound of a rifle-shot all the puffins flew out: they looked like a swarm of flies as they circled back from sea.

To the left the grass slope is bounded by a sheer rock wall about 800 feet high, plastered with gannets on every ledge. One of our party stayed to count them: his estimate was slightly over 4000 pairs.

The steep grass continues on and on at the same angle for 1200 feet. At its top is a range of pinnacles that might have been designed by Doré; and the other side of the island is a sheer rock face, crowded with sea-birds. One of our party was a great enthusiast for Foula: but he admitted that Foula was beaten by Boreray.

Getting aboard again was complicated by the problem of the sheep that had been shot and gralloched. With considerable labour it was brought down a thousand feet to the edge of the rocks: but then what? The old boatman shouted up to throw it in: the land-party averred it would sink. After much argument it was pushed off, and rolled, flailing its limbs, precipitously into the sea. It floated, and was safely hauled in over the dinghy's stern.

We cruised home under the western face. From below, the fantastic quality of the cliff was still more apparent, and the two stacks came into their own. You tend to discount the cliff scenery of St. Kilda until a near view or a special angle obtrudes its super-normal scale upon you and forces you to readjust your ideas. These two stacks, from the top of Hirta or to the approaching yacht, seemed just a pair of unusually fine rocks. As we rounded the southern point, we realized that we were confronted with dimensions new to our experience. A glance at the chart showed us that this was indeed true. The lower of the two, Stac Lee, is 544 feet high—30 feet higher than the top of Beachy Head. The other, Stac an

Armin, rises to well over 600 feet, but has not quite the same grandeur of form.

Stac Lee must be one of the most majestic sea rocks in existence.[1] It rises out of deep water, and as you sail within a few yards of the black mass it gives you a gasping lift, like a cathedral or a flight of rockets. At one place it even overhangs. Its shape too is magnificent—a great blade of rock, somewhat longer than broad, yet not so thin as to convey any impression of fragility. Hosts of similes poured into my mind. At first I thought of the emerging prong of a sea-god's trident, the crude and gigantic emblem of some northern Poseidon. Then suddenly I had it—it was like one of the great stones at Avebury (those early megaliths to my mind so much more impressive than those of Stonehenge), magnified some fifty diameters and erected out of sheer bravado in the sea.

Its top is bevelled off diagonally, and this sloping plane is white with densely packed gannets; gannet ledges lace the black face obliquely with white, and guillemots and kittiwakes inhabit the lesser projections.

Gannets inhabit 21 distinct colonies, from the St. Lawrence to the Bass, from Iceland to southern Ireland. This single colony of Boreray comprises about a fifth of all the gannets in the world. Two separate estimates have given concordant figures—about 17,000 breeding pairs: with the non-breeders, about 40,000 of these enormous and spectacular birds.

Stac Lee looks wholly inaccessible. As a matter of fact, it was much more easily and more often climbed by the St. Kildans than Stac an Armin. There is a relatively easy landing, and a ledge leading diagonally upwards. They came there regularly every year to catch the young gannets for their winter provisions.

The human biology of St. Kilda is as remarkable as its birds. I should say *was*, not *is*, for in 1930 its entire pop-

[1] Professor P. A. Buxton has since told me of Ball's Pyramid, off Lord Howe Island, between Australia and New Zealand. This is 1816 feet in height, but though immensely impressive, is rather a rocky islet than a single rock.

ulation was evacuated, thus closing a chapter which had
been begun before the historic period. Human and avian
biology were indeed inextricably interwoven on St. Kilda.
The human population was essentially parasitic on the birds.
Fishing was never popular, and its results quite subsidiary.
It is true that sheep also played a prominent part in the
island economy, that there were a few cattle, and that
barley, oats, and potatoes were grown; nevertheless, without
the birds the human beings could neither have fed themselves nor paid their dues.

The total number of inhabitants seems never to have
reached 200. It suffered a marked diminution in the early
eighteenth century. Between 1758 and 1855 it fluctuated
between 87 and 120, and after that between 70 and 80.
Inbreeding was avoided through the occasional arrival of
refugees or of exiles banished from the mainland as unde-
sirables. (In 1732 the unfortunate Lady Grange, whose
husband disliked and feared her, was kidnapped, and after
being detained on the island of Heiskeir near North Uist
for three years, was spirited away to the safer prison of
St. Kilda, where she remained for eight years more.)

The birds on which they chiefly relied were gannets,
fulmars, puffins, and, to a lesser extent, guillemots. Puffins
were sometimes caught in their burrows with the aid of a
dog, but usually snared in a noose at the end of a long
rod. They formed the chief meat diet of the islanders in
summer. A puffin was generally boiled in porridge "to give
the porridge a flavour"—an aim which was without doubt
realized!

The gannets were very much sought after for winter
provender. Young gannets, like the young of some other
sea-birds, become extremely fat and at one stage actually
surpass the adults considerably in weight. Their parents
then abandon them. After living on their fat for some days,
hunger prompts them to try their wings, and they throw
themselves off the ledge to volplane into the sea.

Each year up to the 1870's the St. Kildans made an
expedition to Boreray at the time when the "gougs," as the
fat young are called, were most abundant. They knocked

one or two thousand on the head, and brought them back to be salted down against winter. Later, the raids were not so regular, and fewer gougs were taken.

But the fulmar was the St. Kildans' great standby. Like the puffin, fulmars were snared in nooses; but unlike puffins, fulmars often breed on steep places, and great skill and daring was needed, as with the gannets, to obtain a full supply.

The carcasses were salted down for winter, the feathers were plucked and used to stuff mattresses, and the oil was employed to give light during winter. Both oil and feathers were also exported to pay the laird's rent.

The fulmar's oil is a very peculiar phenomenon. Fulmars feed on fish and plankton; the oil from these is retained in the stomach, whence the bird can bring it up and eject it at an enemy. The oil has a nauseous smell, and so potent a weapon is it that no other bird, not even the much larger bonxies or the formidable greater black-backed gull, will try conclusions with a fulmar. If it hits your clothes, they will stink for days. I must confess that when, as I was scrambling along some precipitous slope, I heard the disgusting retching noise made by a fulmar bringing up her ammunition, I tended automatically to dodge out of range in a way not always conducive to safe foothold.

One of the most curious things about the fulmar's oil is its abundance. The average yield per bird is stated to be nearly half a pint. The St. Kildans, after noosing a bird, squeezed the oil out of its mouth into a bag made of a gannet's stomach, and so transported it home.

The island is dotted with little stone beehive huts, called "cletts." These served to store the carcasses and feathers of birds until they were needed, and also to hold turves, potatoes, and grain. We came on one at 1100 feet on a promontory jutting out from the great cliff-face of Conachair.

There are many curious and interesting facts about St. Kilda which one does not want to pass over. The great Dr. Johnson once told Boswell to buy the island so that they might live there for a time—a project which, perhaps fortunately, was never carried out.

One of Dr. Johnson's pronouncements concerned the famous "boat-cough" of St. Kilda, the disease, occasionally fatal, which seized the islanders every time that a boat arrived from the mainland. It is obvious enough to-day that this was due to the absence of germs on St. Kilda and the consequent absence of immunity to colds and flu among the St. Kildans. But even Seton, in 1878, with similar facts from Tristan da Cunha before him, could suggest, as an alternative to contagion, that the ailment might be caused "by a feverish excitement arising from the contact of a higher with a lower civilization"! So we need not be surprised that Dr. Johnson was sceptical. "How can there be a physical effect without a physical cause? . . . If one stranger gives them one cold, two strangers must give them two colds, and so in proportion." But he praised Macaulay, the chronicler of the islands, a great-uncle of the historian, for his broad-mindedness, as a Whig, in insisting on the existence of so miraculous and irrational a phenomenon.

In the early eighteenth century the women wore no shoes or stockings save a sock or feather-shoe made out of the skin of a gannet's neck and back of the head: such a shoe lasted four or five days. They were indeed bird people.

A curious fact about the St. Kildans is that they did not use real peat, but only turf. This may be partly explained by the peat-bogs being at a height of over 1000 feet above the village, but is certainly curious, since by cutting turf they damaged the grazing for their beasts as well as restricting themselves to a very inferior fuel.

The subject of grazing brings me to the Soay sheep. These are of great interest as being in all probability the most primitive domestic breed in existence, showing the least modification from their wild ancestor. They are not so large, nor are their horns so fine, but in general their resemblance to Mouflon and other wild species is much closer than to any other domestic breed. They have the same long legs and small bodies, the same active carriage, the same general colouration (a light reddish-brown with light rump), the same short hair, only an inch or so long, with dense underwool, the same fringe of long hair on the throat. They are quite different from the Hebridean breed.

Nothing certain is known of their history, but it may be taken that they represent a very early stage in Western man's moulding of the wild sheep into a wool-bearing, mutton-producing machine, a stage which everywhere else was supplanted by improved breeds, but survived in St. Kilda because of its remoteness. To see them scampering about the cliffs and steep slopes of the islands is to be transported far back in human cultural history, perhaps to 3000 or 4000 B.C.

One of the most remarkable facts in recent European natural history is the steady spread of the fulmar. In the Faeroes, its arrival between 1816 and 1839 was followed by a period of rapid increase, which has continued until the present. In recent years about 100,000 fulmars have been taken annually for food in the Faeroes.

In Britain it was not known to breed outside St. Kilda. However, the wave of increase began to operate here too, and in 1878 it colonized Foula off the Shetlands. By 1891 it had reached the main part of the Shetland archipelago, and by the turn of the century was breeding in Orkney and Sutherland. To-day it is prospecting breeding-sites as far south as Land's End and the Scillies on the west, and Dorset and the Isle of Wight on the south, and is already breeding at Flamborough Head on the east.

There are now about 21,000 pairs on St. Kilda, while those on the rest of our coast are estimated at about 41,000 pairs. Looked at from another angle, the fulmar population of the British Isles has nearly trebled during the last half-century—a rate of increase a little higher than that of the human population of England and Wales during the first half of the nineteenth century.

At one time it was thought that this spectacular increase and extension of range was due to the decrease of human depredations consequent on the introduction of kerosene oil and tinned food. However, James Fisher's exhaustive study of the problem has made it clear that this is not so, and that though the drop in the human population of St. Kilda in the '50's and '60's may have had a local influence,

the main cause must be a biological one, some as yet un-
explained factor favouring fulmar survival and spread
throughout the range of the species.

The gannets, meanwhile, had not multiplied to the same
extent. The young gannets were the St. Kildans' greatest
delicacy and their capture the islanders' greatest sport. As
the birds lay only one egg, and their total numbers were
probably rather less than to-day, their numbers were held
severely in check. But since about 1890 the gannet too has
embarked on a period of increase—not so striking as that
of the fulmar, but none the less definite. Two quite new
colonies have been established in the Shetlands, and there
has been a marked increase in the numbers of birds in the
Irish and Welsh colonies. For the last quarter-century, the
increase is in the neighbourhood of 15 per cent. In this
case, too, there seems to have been a wave of biological increase affecting the species as a whole, in addition to any
local effects caused by the St. Kildans' changed habits.

One of the chief aims of our party was to estimate the
number of gannets on St. Kilda and two other rarely-visited
breeding colonies. This was part of the scheme organized
by James Fisher and Gwynne Vevers for the enumeration
of the world population of gannets—the first occasion on
which a complete census has been taken of any wide-ranging
wild species.

The layman may well ask how gannets are counted. The
first sight of a big colony is bewildering, and a census would
seem impossible. However, it is eminently possible, as repeated counts by separate observers have shown. The simplest and best method of counting gannets is just to count
them. Each observer takes a section of cliff, and goes over
it with his glasses, ledge by ledge, counting the number of
breeding pairs. One bird is always on the nest: when both
are present they will be close together, so that a pair can
be distinguished from the separate sitters.

Direct counting, however, is difficult or impossible from
the sea, unless in a dead calm. You then have to count birds
on some especially favourable section, and estimate the
proportion which this bears to the total area occupied by

nesting birds. In some cases a photographic method is the best—telephoto photographs are taken, and the birds counted on enlargements from them.

Experience shows that direct counts in favourable circumstances are accurate to 2 or 3 per cent.; and it can be taken that the world figure (which provisionally may be put at 166,000 birds) will be accurate certainly to within 10 and probably to about 5 per cent.

The other two gannetries which we visited were Sule Stack and Sula Sgeir. They form part of a chain of small islands whose very existence is unknown to most people, strung out some twenty-five to forty miles off the northern Scottish coast—Sule Skerry, with its lighthouse, Sule Stack with 3500 pairs of gannets, North Rona, the greatest breeding-ground of Atlantic seals in Britain, of which Dr. Fraser Darling has written, and Sula Sgeir, with another 4000 pairs of gannets. Sule or Sula is, of course, from the same root as Solan in Solan Goose, the gannet's alternative name, and is the Gaelic for gannet.

Sule Stack is wonderfully impressive considering its small size—a bare 125 feet in height—or perhaps because of it. It is an outpost of the land, upthrust out of the hostile sea, teeming with life, yet a life alien (though not hostile) to ours, northern, remote, with its own quality and its own values. It reminded me of Tom's visit to Mother Carey in Kingsley's *Water Babies*—Mother Carey who made things make themselves—a workshop of animate nature.

The highest point rises up curved to hook over in an overhang, sheer above a sloping slab, like a wave immortalized in rock. The rock is black, with the white of breaking waves round its base, and its higher parts frosted over with the white of gannets.

It was too rough to land here, but on Sula Sgeir we managed to put one man ashore, though the swell was enough to warrant lifebelts for the dinghy party. Sula Sgeir seems to be the only gannetry in Britain whose numbers have gone down in the last seven years. This is without doubt due to the fact that it is also the only gannetry which is still raided for young birds: almost every year an expedition sets out from Ness, in the north of Lewis, and kills between one and two thousand gougs for food. It is to be hoped that public opinion and the County Council will put a stop to this practice.

Another objective of our trip was to fill in some blanks in the census of bridled guillemots. "Bridled" or "spectacled" guillemots differ from the normal in having a white rim with a hindward prolongation round each eye. They are not a distinct species or subspecies, as was at one time supposed, but a mendelian variety which interbreeds freely with the normal. In the books they are usually described as rare aberrations. So they are in the south of Britain: but about half-way along our coast their numbers begin to increase. On the Farnes they make up 5 per cent. of the total; on the Orkneys 10 to 13; in the Shetlands 23 to 26; while in Iceland and Bear Island they are well over 50 per cent., and thus constitute the normal type, while our normal is there the aberration.

What the precise meaning of the phenomenon may be is as yet obscure. Either the bridled variety is a new and advantageous mutation which is extending its numbers and range at the expense of the normal (as has happened with the black variety of the brush-tailed opossum in Tasmania), or there is a balance of advantage between the two types; the bridled being favoured in cooler and more humid regions, the normal in warm and dry conditions (as occurs with the black and grey varieties of the hamster in Russia). The diminution in the percentage of bridled birds on the less humid north coast of Iceland seems to speak in favour of this latter explanation.

In any case, the first step is clearly to map the distribution of bridling accurately, and to see whether it changes with the passage of time.

St. Kilda was one of the places for which very few data were available. The guillemot ledges here are not easily accessible, but we managed to count nearly a thousand birds and to find that the percentage was about 16, much higher than anticipated. An intensive afternoon on Handa, just south of Cape Wrath, yielded a count of over 3000, and confirmed the previous estimate within 0.5 per cent.

The end of our trip deserves record as illustrating the difficulties of communication that still keep the western isles so remote. One of our party wanted to be back in London for a Monday evening meeting. We pushed across through the night from St. Kilda to reach the west of Lewis early on Saturday, caught a bus in to Stornoway—to find that there was no possibility whatever of arriving in time. No boat sails on Saturday night, as this would desecrate the Sabbath: and the Sunday night boat was too late.

We explored Stornoway and its wooded park, one of the only two woods in the Hebrides; slept aboard the boat, set off soon after dawn on Sunday, visited Sula Sgeir and North Rona, and sailed through the night to Loch Erriboll. There we found that a bus recorded on the time-table was in reality non-existent; cadged a lift on a road foreman's car to Durness, found a car at the local hotel (which had on its notepaper "Railway Station: Lairg, 58 miles"); caught the train at Lairg; explored Inverness between trains; and reached London before the letters we had posted in Stornoway.

Communications may be difficult: but it is very well worth while overcoming the difficulties. The north of Scotland and its western and northern fringe of islands constitute a region where the Arctic fauns overlaps the temperate. Whooper swans and great northern divers and Sclavonian grebes have invaded it from the north, and the mainland forms have thrown out outposts to the islands and beyond them to the Faeroes and Iceland. It teems with life: the birds outnumber the human inhabitants many-fold, and their congregations on the bird rocks are not easily to be surpassed. Seals bob up wherever you anchor, and it is a poor day when you do not see a school of porpoises or small whales and some 25-foot basking sharks. It has a unique history and pressing human problems of a dwindling population, top-heavy with old people.

To the biologists and naturalists of Britain it is a laboratory on the doorstep of their own country where they can find an inexhaustible store of material for the study of evolution in action.

ANIMAL PESTS IN WAR-TIME

MAN'S struggle for existence falls under three heads: his struggle with the forces of the inorganic environment, his struggle with other species of organisms, and his struggle with his own works and his own nature.

It is this last aspect of the struggle which has come to bulk larger in recent times; the economic and social forces generated by human systems have taken the bit in their teeth and threaten to pull the fabric of civilization down if not harnessed and controlled, while at the same time new manifestations of cruelty and lust for power, organized on an unprecedented scale, have arisen as monsters to be fought and overcome. Meanwhile the struggle with the inorganic world has become progressively less important during history: indeed, apart from occasional tornadoes, floods, and earthquakes, the inorganic forces have been mastered, and the old struggle has been in the main converted into a drive for increased mastery.

The struggle with other organisms, however, continues. It changes its character as civilization progresses. Every new advance in civilization, while it may knock out one set of competitors, often favours new ones. To take a simple example, the invention of agriculture was an invitation to the hordes of plant-eating insects, snails, birds, and mammals: from being neutrals in man's struggle, they become his enemies. In a similar way, the crowding of human beings into walled cities was an invitation to various bacteria and other microscopic parasites: organisms which previously had been a minor nuisance could now spread with explosive rapidity to generate violent plagues and become major enemies of man.

The new situations created by this war have provided new opportunities for various animal enemies. It is of some interest to mention some of the problems that have arisen, and the degree of success achieved by research and practical control measures in coping with them. Most of the inquiries have been carried out under one or other of our official research bodies, the Agricultural Research Council, the Department of Scientific and Industrial Research, and the Medical Research Council.

The rabbit has undergone perhaps the most extraordinary changes of status of any common animal. It is no more a native of Britain than of Australia. Though there are some who still maintain that it was brought over by the Romans, it is almost certain that its introduction was due to the Normans. Far from spreading rapidly to became a pest, as occurred in Australia when the British re-exported it thither nearly a millennium later, it had during some centuries to be sedulously looked after, and warrens constituted valuable properties, chiefly on account of the fur provided by the rabbits. How is it, then, that the rabbit is to-day a serious pest in Britain? The answer, I think, is simple. It is due to the increase of population, the spread of agriculture, and later of game-preserving. This brought about the total destruction of many predators over most of Britain and the reduction in numbers of many others. The large birds of prey and the large carnivores have suffered most; and they were natural enemies of the rabbit. Intensive game-preservation, with its wholesale reduction of stoats and weasels, was the last straw.

However, the rabbit has up till recently been in a peculiar double-edged position—not merely a pest, but also a property. Rabbit-killing was an important source of minor income for many farmers; and the gain, in the parlous state of British agriculture, often outweighed the loss due to their depredations. Now the war has again altered the balance. Home-grown food is urgently needed; and the rabbit has become, wholly and officially, a pest.

Research has also provided means for dealing with the pest. A course of fairly intensive trapping, followed by gassing with cyanide gas in the burrows, will destroy all rabbits. Originally an expensive pump was supposed to be necessary for gassing. Now it has been shown that a long spoon can be used to put the chemical down the burrows, which are then blocked; and this little technical improvement has brought the method within the reach of all. There is now no reason why Britain, or at least all its important farming land, should not be brought back to its pre-Conquest freedom from rabbits.

Among other rodents, the two species of rat are the most serious pests. They, like rabbits, are being studied by the Bureau of Animal Population at Oxford. War-research has shown that the population of the common brown rat was kept at a high level by its capacity to breed throughout the winter in corn-stacks. This can be prevented if threshing is done early and all rats that then emerge are killed. The fixing of the price of corn has encouraged early threshing, and the killing of rats at threshing-time is now compulsory under a statutory order. By these measures, in combination with a large-scale poisoning campaign, it should be possible to reduce the rural rat population so materially as to transform it from a serious pest to a minor nuisance.

The black rat, like the rabbit, has suffered strange vicissitudes of status. It was for centuries the only species of rat in Britain, although it too was originally introduced (probably at the time of the Crusades). When, however, the brown rat was later introduced in the eighteenth century, it proved more successful save in the few situations where the black rat's greater climbing abilities and lesser dependence on water gave it an advantage; and the black rat became virtually confined to shipboard. Recently, the increase of high buildings, and the attempts to proof them against the brown rat, have given the black rat a new chance, and it has become a serious pest in ports and port warehouses. But careful study has now been made of the species, and this, with new methods of poisoning based on pre-baiting, is apparently providing the basis for effective control—an important matter not only because of its food depredations, but because of the danger of its introducing plague.

In all matters concerning pests, they key to control is the

study of populations—their absolute size, their reproduction and the checks to it. The wireworm will illustrate this point very clearly. Wireworm is the popular name for the grubs of various species of clickbeetle. They are all but universally present in agricultural land, especially in old pastures, and one of the great problems of this war is to decide which pastures should be ploughed up. If they contain too many wireworms, there is no chance of a crop for some years. The usual methods of sampling enable a reasonably good forecast to be made; but they detect only the larger grubs. Recently, new and ingenious methods have been devised by which all the wireworms in a sample of soil can be separated from the soil particles and the fragments of vegetation and counted.

The astonishing result emerges that the wireworm population may reach ten and even twenty millions per acre! Above about five millions per acre, it is no good ploughing up, for any crop; up to two millions it will be tolerably safe for cereals; and below 500,000 the damage will be negligible.

The accurate counting method has another advantage. The total population can be separated into four size-groups, corresponding to the produce of the four successive years that each grub lives in the soil before it turns into a beetle. And this, as will be readily seen, enables one to forecast the future. If, for instance, the youngest-but-one age-group is abnormally abundant, the dangerous time will be two years hence, for it is the large grubs which do the most damage.

The war has brought wireworms into the limelight by the need to plough up old grassland. Similarly the early realization of our precarious food position, and the consequent building-up of huge reserves, has accorded special prominence to the all-too-numerous insect pests of stored products —grain, oil-cake, chocolate, and many other materials. The great majority of these are introduced species, with their original home in the tropics or sub-tropics. Accordingly, they are unable to maintain themselves in the open in this country, and so are not dangerous to growing crops.

The serious pests are those which can breed in the artificial environment of granaries and other stores. And again, as with the brown rat, one of the chief methods of control is to cut down the amount of breeding that goes on: below a certain level of numbers, the flour-beetles and weevils and the like are an annoyance rather than a serious danger. Here, cleanliness and order are the chief weapons. Where spilt grain and old sacks are allowed to lie about, the creatures can breed in odd corners. Thus scrupulous cleanliness and tidiness will prevent the corners of the warehouse itself from becoming permanent breeding-grounds; for this, vacuum cleaners with special nozzles are useful.

Further, even a slightly infested sack, if left to itself for a long time, becomes a teeming homeland from which colonists spread in all directions. So delivery in strict rotation is essential; if this is adhered to, no package has the chance to become heavily infested before it is used. Cleanliness, however, is not enough. Deliberate destruction is also necessary. For this, the chemist and the applied biologist must work hand in hand—the chemist to produce improved gases for fumigation, the biologist to make sure that the infestable materials are not damaged, whether in their flavour or in their capacity for use (as with the bread-making qualities of flour). Considerable progress has been made in this field, and once more the goal is in sight—in this case, the goal of pest-free stores and stored materials. The pest species, we can be sure, will never be exterminated, since they are constantly being re-introduced; but they can be so reduced as to cease being pests.

The external parasites of man constitute a rather different type of pest. The only one of major importance in Britain is the louse. This repulsive little creature is not only extremely unpleasant and irritating, but a potential source of great danger as being the carrier for the germ of typhus. For war may bring about conditions in which many people have to share crowded sleeping-quarters, cannot change their clothes regularly, and often have to go without washing; and these conditions favour both the breeding of lice and their transference to a widening circle of hosts. In the last war it was the trenches which favoured the spread of the louse among soldiers; in this war it was the public air-raid shelters and the conditions of evacuation which favoured its spread in the civil populations.

In the last war excellent de-lousing methods were devised for the troops as they came out of the line, and these were sufficient to keep the danger of typhus from materializing. But they merely removed the lice from a man and his clothes; he and they could be at once re-infested when he went back. The problem for this war was to find some means of keeping people louse-free for considerable periods; at the London School of Hygiene and Tropical Medicine great progress has been made with this. The details cannot at this stage be made public, but the method opens up the pos-sibility of eradicating lice from the British fauna, and may be of great importance on the continent of Europe after the war in preventing outbreaks of typhus.

One minor tragedy of the present war is that it has put that magnificent bird, the peregrine falcon, into the category of a pest. This is because planes patrolling our coasts must communicate with headquarters, but cannot do so by wire-less since this would give their position away to the enemy. Carrier pigeons are accordingly used, and these fall ready victims to peregrines. Over a considerable stretch of coast, the peregrines have therefore had to be killed off. It is hoped that the wandering propensities of the species (from which it gets its name) will enable these areas to be re-colonized when peace comes.

The general impression of war research on these problems, is that real progress has been made, and that in this field at least the grim necessities of war will have brought permanent advances for peace.

TENNESSEE REVISITED: THE TECHNIQUE
OF DEMOCRATIC PLANNING

WE HAVE often been told that over-all planning is incompatible with democratic freedom and individual initiative. That notion lingers on in considerable strength in the U.S.A. Planning, according to the enemies of the New Deal, is the thin end of the totalitarian wedge: once start to plan, and you have embarked upon the dangerous road that leads on inevitably to "100 per cent. planning" and the end of democracy. This is curious, because it is precisely in the U.S.A. that planning has been most conspicuously and most successfully democratic. The best examples are in the Tennessee Valley and in the North-West Region along the Columbia River.

In 1935 I made a special journey to study the working of the Tennessee Valley Authority. The TVA, one of the earliest fruits of Roosevelt's New Deal, was then less than two years old; but even in its infancy it was impressive in its size and scope. Its physical impressiveness is greater to-day, now that the grandiose series of dams and power plants serving an area nearly the size of England is approaching completion. But what interested me most when I revisited the area in the spring of 1942 was the technique which the TVA has adopted with the deliberate aim of reconciling over-all planning with the values of democracy.

For its specific task of building dams for navigation and flood-control, with the large-scale generation of electric power as a corollary, it was given precise terms of reference. But it was also assigned the more general aim of initiating experiments for the general development of the region—in other words, of making and executing a comprehensive over-all plan.

In such a situation, the planner's temptation is to believe so much in his plan that he insists on imposing it from above, as it stands, and as quickly as possible. This is the temptation which leads to "beneficent dictatorships." The planner, remembering that power corrupts, must resist it, as Christ did when the devil offered him power over all the kingdoms of the earth.

The TVA, thanks to the wise guidance of H. A. Morgan and David Lilienthal, has refused to yield to this temptation, and has increasingly set itself to devising techniques for planning by persuasion, consent, and participation.

Let me give some examples. In the agricultural sphere it was essential that the appalling soil erosion should be checked. For this it was necessary to change the attitude and methods of the farmers. Mineral fertilizers must be used; check-dams built; contour ploughing adopted to prevent run-off; new crops introduced; the erosion-prone slopes put back to forest or laid down to grass.

The method adopted has been to persuade farmers to use their farms as demonstrations of TVA fertilizers and TVA methods. The County Agricultural Agent (who himself combines Federal, State, and County functions, and whose assistant is paid by the TVA) calls together the farmers of a community and explains the problem. The farmers themselves then select the farm of one of their group to be used as a demonstration unit. The work is done with the co-operation of the local farmers' Committee and the County Agent or his assistant. In return for this help and for the fertilizers provided by the TVA, the farmer agrees to carry out the programme for a definite period, to adjust his farming methods (for instance, by planting soil-protective crops and using contour terracing where there is danger of erosion), to keep records and report results, and to pay the freight costs of the fertilizers provided.

In such cases the test-demonstration farm becomes a focal point of community interest, a real community enterprise, carried on and to a large extent planned by the farmers themselves. After six years there were over 26,000 demonstration farms of this type in existence.

Sometimes a keen group will transform the methods of

a whole county in two or three years. But elsewhere there may be more resistance. I was taken to one lone demonstration farm in an area where an enterprising young man was the only farmer in the community willing to participate in the TVA's programme. Five years ago he had bought his farm for $1200: as a result of TVA fertilizer, TVA advice, and his own initiative, he improved it to such good purpose that last year he was offered $4500 for it.

The neighbours had at first been wholly unco-operative, and his successes had been sceptically dismissed as mere luck. Now, however, after five years, conviction was creeping in, and they too were beginning to adopt the new-fangled methods. This is slow going; but it is sure. It is exasperating to see old error persisted in so long. But once the resistance is overcome, the new methods are taken over with enthusiasm.

Administratively, too, the TVA is careful not to tread on the toes of existing agencies. In agriculture, the TVA co-operates with County, State, and Federal Agencies. It works mainly through the "Land-Grant Colleges" of the region—State institutions backed by Federal Funds, with which it has an over-all agreement embodied in a "Memorandum of Understanding." Thus the TVA might give funds for some special job for testing new phosphatic fertilizers manufactured in its great fertilizer plant at Muscle Shoals. If so, the Land Grant Colleges would carry out the tests and appoint the personnel, who would, however, have to be approved by the TVA's personnel department. Once adequate tests have been made, practical demonstrations are needed; for these, the TVA has entered upon similar agreements with the Agricultural Extension Services operating under the same Colleges.

The same sort of thing has occurred with regard to Wild Life Conservation. The TVA here operates under a formal agreement with the U.S. Bureau of Fisheries, the U.S. Biological Survey, and the Conservation Commissions of the various States in the Valley, and in informal co-operation with the State Universities and many local agencies.

Here is another example from quite a different field. As the result of one of the big dams, the little country town of Guntersville was left on the end of a long narrow peninsula jutting out into a lake. The TVA suggested that the town should set up its own City Planning Commission. It contributed funds to the Alabama State Planning Commission to pay for the services of planning consultants and a resident planning engineer, and has itself furnished much technical advice. By these means the invading water which threatened disaster was turned to advantage. The town was replanned so as to provide docks and facilities for fishing and pleasure-boating. As a result it has become both an important tourist and recreation centre (the local regattas now attract gatherings of 50,000 or more) and a point of trans-shipment for the increasing volume of water-borne goods now finding their way up the Tennessee River, on which navigation was previously almost non-existent.

Here and in many other fields the success of the TVA depends on having a sufficient staff of experts of first-class calibre who can be detailed to help in local problems in the field. But in all cases they help the local community to help itself. They do not impose their own plans, but they catalyse planning jointly with others.

The way in which central planning may be used not to suppress but to stimulate private initiative is illustrated by TVA's action over electrical and agricultural appliances. The big combines and other agricultural machines so essential on the Middle Western prairies would be useless, as well as too expensive, for the small and hilly farms of the Valley. The TVA accordingly set itself to design equipment suitable for its own area. After extensive testing, agreements were drawn up by which manufacturers of farm equipment could make and sell the machines commercially, at an agreed price. A recent example is a multiple-purpose "furrow-seeder" for hilly country. This can be attached to a two-horse plough, ploughs furrows along the contours, and drops seeds and phosphatic fertilizer in the furrow, all in a single operation; and costs less than $25. A similar venture was the perfecting of a cheap refrigerator, selling at a few hundred dollars, to serve entire communities for the storage of meat and other perishable farm commodities.

The general aim of combining the efficiency of central planning with the sense of participation that comes from decentralization is well illustrated in the TVA's electricity programme. Generation and transmission are centralized under the TVA itself. But both the ownership and the management of the distribution are decentralized, and are in the hands of local organizations, either municipal or co-operative. Standards in regard to rates and other important matters are kept uniform by means of the contracts under which TVA provides bulk electric power to the local units; but the separate units have worked out the most ingenious methods for making the new resource available to the maximum number of people in the most fruitful way.

With all this and much of similar import, however, a basic problem remained—how to make the people of the region as a whole feel that the plan was *their* plan, not a scheme imposed from above by a remote authority, nor even a series of special schemes in which particular interests or communities could profitably participate. With this aim in view, a joint committee has been set up, representing the TVA and all the State Universities in the region, to see how best the educational system and its curriculum can be utilized to bring about a wider understanding of the aims and achievements of the TVA, and the general relevance of the plan to the life of the Valley. From the primary school to the University, interest is now being focused on the broad problems of the region, on the plans of the TVA for dealing with them, and on the need for popular co-operation if the plans are to be effective.

This scheme is still young, but it should be of real value in generating a social self-consciousness in the region and relating it to the central authority, which otherwise might remain in Olympian detachment from popular feeling.

In the North-West Region, where the Columbia River is being harnessed on an equally grand scale, popular participation in planning has been taken a step farther back, to the framing of the plan itself. Though I was unable to visit the Columbia Basin personally, I had the opportunity of hearing about the work there from one who had been concerned with it from the start, Professor Kenneth Warner, now at the University of Tennessee.

Planning in the region was begun by the Pacific North-West Regional Planning Commission—one of the two official planning bodies in existence, both of them under the National Resources Planning Board.[1] Some members of this were dissatisfied with the amount of local support for planning, and took the initiative in the formation of a non-official planning body, the North-West Regional Council. This has become a clearing-house for research on regional problems, and has done a great deal to present them to the public, both directly by books and pamphlets and articles, and indirectly through the educational system. In this latter field it conducts short week-end courses and longer "study workshops" for teachers, and has a panel of educational consultants which, as in the TVA, is getting a great deal of material into the curriculum. It also seeks to stimulate the interest of various professional groups. Any plans eventually adopted for this huge region will be more thorough for the work of the Council, and will command much more public interest and backing from the outset.

In specific cases, popular and local participation has already been achieved in detailed practical projects. The best example of this so far is Elma, in the State of Washington. Elma is a little community of under 10,000 people, which had been largely dependent on timber. Over-cutting of the forests resulted in the closing of its one big mill, and the entire area was faced with disaster. The local Chamber of Commerce asked the State Planning Commission to help in investigating their problems. The commission enlisted the further support of the two regional bodies we have already mentioned, the official Commission and the non-

[1] Whose appropriations have been discontinued by Congress since this article was written—a disastrous piece of political folly.

official Council, together with other agencies, and the Elma Survey was initiated. But Elma was not treated as merely a passive subject for investigation. Help was given on the express understanding that the community would participate —and participate it did, on the grand scale.

Picked High School students collected valuable information needed for the survey (incidentally educating themselves in the process); discussions of the town's problems in class led to discussion in the home; the local newspaper gave much space to the survey and its aims; the Chamber of Commerce enlisted the services of all the major business enterprises; and a series of public meetings (rather like the old Town Meetings in New England) were held.

The result was that the people of Elma were brought in from the outset. It was *their* survey and *their* plan; they were behind it, so thoroughly that the town was able to implement certain of the Survey's recommendations even before the report was published.

I cannot end better than by quoting from a recent address of David Lilienthal, the Chairman of the three-man Board of the TVA. The Board, he says, is convinced that "the way of doing the job and the results that have been achieved are inter-dependent"; and accordingly has been experimenting to discover the best means of achieving administrative decentralization as the only means of reconciling planning with democracy. They now feel that the three essential characteristics of a decentralized administration are these. First, it is "one in which the greatest number of decisions is made in the field. . . . An overcentralized administration is always characterized by the fact that its field officers tend to become messengers and office boys. . . . (2) A decentralized administration must develop as far as possible the active participation of the people themselves . . . and encourage the participation of local agencies in establishing basic national standards. . . ."

Thirdly, a decentralized administration must co-ordinate

the work of all other agencies concerned, and "the co-ordination must be in the field."

To these we may perhaps add a fourth—the decentralization of the *idea* behind an administration so that its planning becomes a part of public opinion. This is to be achieved not merely through customary channels of publicity and public relations, but also through the educational system.

Britain is very different from the United States; but the principles and techniques worked out in the Great American planning experiments (not without considerable trial and error) are applicable wherever large-scale planning is needed. In the planned Britain of after the war, we must avoid a congestion of centralized planning in Whitehall, we must encourage the people to feel that it is their plan and that they are helping to make it. This can be done by using the democratic techniques of decentralization, co-operation with other agencies, and popular participation, both in action and in opinion and feeling.

COLONIES IN A CHANGING WORLD

THE world is changing under our eyes. To the accompaniment of much blood-letting, burning of crops, destruction of buildings, hunger, disease, and torture (but also much bravery, devotion, ingenuity, efficiency, and hard thinking), the institutions and ideas of a historical epoch are on their way into the discard. Unlimited national sovereignty, *laisser-faire* liberalism, unrestricted capitalist enterprise, neutrality, the police state, free trade, are swirling irrevocably down the cosmic drain.

In such a confusion of change, the colonies are bound to be involved. The world's conscience is beginning to grow a little uneasy over the fact of one country "possessing" another as a colony, just as it grew uneasy a century or so ago over the fact of one human being possessing another as a slave. The inter-war disputation between the "have" and the "have-not" powers is wearing a bit thin. It is beginning to dawn on us that the real "have-nots" are the colonial peoples themselves.

The mercantilist view of colonies as milch-cows to be exploited for the benefit of the metropolitan power, when looked at firmly in the light of post-depression economics, is seen to be as short-sighted as it was selfish; not merely to provide a moral basis for their dependent empires, but to increase general prosperity, the standard of living of the native colonial peoples (nearly an eighth of the world's population) must imperatively be raised. The principle of trusteeship sounded rather noble when applied to mandates in 1919; but now, even if it were to be adopted for all colonies, it would look inadequate. The only possible substitute for imperialism is seen to be the development—political and social as well as economic—of the areas now classed as colonies. What is more, the development must be undertaken internationally. The separate possession of colonies was an inevitable consequence or extension of the game of power politics as played by independent sovereign states; whatever international framework is superposed upon nationalism after this war, it must concern itself with the colonies as well as with the advanced nations on which the colonies depend.

Colonies in the broad sense of the word may enjoy the status of Crown colonies, protectorates, condominiums, mandated territories of various categories, and so forth. But they all share one essential feature—they are politically dependent territories, administered from the capital of a colonial power. They have their own governors and legislative councils; but there is almost invariably an "official majority" on the Council, consisting of local Civil Servants and administrators; and there is normally little representation of the native population on the Council, and that little is in most cases indirect, often through a white missionary (as well as via the Commissioner for Native Affairs).

Colonies may be best classified by political type. In the first place, there are the relatively advanced colonies which are clearly destined in the near future to follow countries like Iraq and to emerge from political dependence into the condition of partial or complete self-government. Syria, Palestine, and the Philippines are obvious examples, while Ceylon (like non-colonies such as India and Burma) is a clear candidate for a fairly speedy attainment of Dominion status. Ethiopia, after its brief interlude as an Italian colony, has now been restored to independence, but (as with other somewhat backward territories) its independence will be qualified for some time to come by a certain amount of advice and help and tutelage from the white man.

Northern Africa constitutes a special area. Already before the war, Algeria and Northern Libya were for most purposes integral parts of France and Italy respectively: Algeria, in fact, was virtually a French *département*. In any case, the whole of the North African littoral, with its hinterland back to the Sahara, is historically a part of the Mediterranean economy and culture, and may be expected to become linked with increasing closeness to the general European system.

Among the remainder, a number have been retained as colonies wholly or mainly for strategic reasons. Gibraltar, Malta, and Hawaii are the most obvious cases, while Aden, Guam, Hong Kong, and the illicitly fortified Japanese mandates in the Marshall and Caroline Islands are other examples. Cyprus, British Malaya, Dakar, and many other territories are of value as much for strategic as for other reasons. The strategic importance of the West Indies and Newfoundland for the Western hemisphere has been acknowledged in the arrangements made for leasing bases to the United States, and the Anglo-American occupation of Iceland has *de facto* converted that island into a strategic colony of the United Nations, the Malta of the North Atlantic.

The future of strategic colonies will depend primarily upon the arrangements made after the war for guaranteeing international security. The most likely guess seems to be that they will develop, through a stage of pooled strategic strong-points shared by some or all of the United Nations, into truly international bases at the disposal of whatever Security League comes into existence.

Even when the advanced and the strategic colonies are eliminated, the bulk of colonial territories remain to be considered—the whole of tropical Africa including Madagascar, the West Indies, the Netherlands East Indies, Malaya, New Guinea, Greenland, and various islands in the Pacific. They all share one characteristic—cultural, social, and economic backwardness; and the colonial problem is primarily the problem of abolishing this backwardness. Most colonial territories would never have become colonies if they had not been so backward.

In Britain during the war, in spite of all the urgencies of the military situation, there has been a great revival of interest in the colonial question. Different groups naturally arrive at different solutions; but the general direction of progressive opinion is remarkably uniform. First, it presupposes a necessary minimum of international organization, to guarantee security from military aggression,. and to promote economic stability. Secondly, it rejects the pooling of colonies under an international body. Instead, it envisages the adherence of all colonial powers to a colonial charter, the raising of administrative and labour standards by a series of international conventions, and the general supervision of colonial administration by an international Colonial Commission. Thirdly, and most important, it regards the development of the tropical colonies as one of the major economic priorities before the world.

The question is how to raise their mode of existence at optimum speed toward a new level. I have deliberately used the phrase *optimum* in place of *maximum* speed. In the case of advanced societies it suffices to prescribe the desirable direction of movement; for tropical areas it is also necessary to discover the optimum rate of change. When the advance to be made is not merely from one level of civilization to the next, but from a pre-mechanical, analphabetic, primitive tribal society, operating in untamed natural surroundings, to a technological and highly educated civilization which has largely controlled and even created its own physical environment, it is extremely easy to move too fast: change, like food, must be provided in assimilable doses. Equally, it is easy for change in one field to get quite out of step with other sets of changes, so distorting and disturbing the whole process. Thus in some areas concentration on economic exploitation has resulted in enormous labour migrations which have not only drained the native reserves of the menfolk needed for subsistence agriculture and a balanced life, but at the other end have brought into being a dingy, discontented, and atomized black proletariat, which, on any standard of ultimate human values, represents a regression from traditional tribal existence.

Let me begin with the political aspect. The favourite solution of idealist constitution-mongerers has been the immediate pooling of all colonies under the administration of an international authority. This, however, is in reality not only impracticable but undesirable. No international authority which we can contemplate as possible in the near future could be adequate to undertake the full executive responsibility demanded of an administration, and the existing colonial powers would rightly refuse to hand over their responsibilities to such an organization. Furthermore, colonial administration is a difficult business, demanding a homogeneous staff with its own traditions and accumulated experience. The handing over of administration to a mixed international staff unsupported by strong central machinery would in many cases cause a retrogression in the handling of native problems, and this might well have quite serious effects in some areas. There is also the significant fact that articulate native opinion, backed by such bodies as the Aborigines Protection Society, is almost entirely hostile to internationalization; they feel that this might readily become a more dangerous and impersonal means of exploitation of blacks or browns by white than the existing system. Further, some of the more developed tropical colonies, such as the Gold Coast and the West Indies, have in fact developed a strong loyalty to their metropolitan country and would strongly resent any change in allegiance.

No, the detailed business of administration must for the immediate future remain in the hands of strong and highly developed nations. What is more, transfer of colonies from one power to another is to be avoided wherever possible. It makes for instability, and it treats the colonies as pawns in the political game.

Another widely mooted suggestion has been the universal adoption of a strengthened Mandate principle. After the last war, the ex-German colonies were transferred to other powers, not as outright possessions, but as Mandates from the League of Nations. The system involved the formal acceptance of the principle of trusteeship. The Mandatory Power was to administer the mandated territory in the interests of the native inhabitants until such time as they

were capable of self-government, just as a trustee administers
a ward's estate until he becomes of age. Largely under the
influence of Lord Lugard, this simple idea of trusteeship
was gradually replaced by what he called the Dual Mandate.
Under this concept the trustee preserves a dual responsibility
—toward the native inhabitants, to encourage their progress
toward greater prosperity and self-government, and toward
the rest of the world, to make the resources of the area generally available.

The Mandatory Powers had to give an annual account
of their stewardship to the Mandates Commission of the
League, a body which included representatives of non-
colonial as well as of Colonial powers.

The mandate system did produce certain valuable results.
It has on occasion prevented undesirable action. The French,
for instance, made one or two attempts to extend to their
mandates their strongly protectionist imperial system, with
the trade of the colonies tied to that of the metropolitan
country, but this has always been successfully resisted by the
Mandates Commission. The standard of administration demanded in a mandated territory has inevitably had repercussions on the colonies of the same power. It has always
aided public opinion, both at Geneva and perhaps even more
in the home Parliaments, in keeping Governments up to
the mark.

The suggestion has therefore been made that all colonies
should be given the status of Mandates, and that at the
same time the Mandates Commission should be strengthened
both in its research and secretarial staff and in its powers.

There are, however, a number of objections to this course.
In many quarters, not only in ex-enemy countries, the
Mandate system as introduced in 1919 was regarded as little
more than a pious veneer for annexation. Then the term
has become, rightly or wrongly, associated with the idea
of transfer of territories from one power to another, which
would be bitterly resisted by various colonial powers as well
as being undesirable in itself. Again, in certain quarters,
including the educated natives of various colonies, it has

acquired a connotation of inferior status. And finally the principle of trusteeship itself is regarded as inadequate to modern conditions. Lord Hailey, the author of the great *African Survey,* has said in recent addresses that the idea of trusteeship is too legalistic and negative, too much a survival from the *laisser-faire* epoch. Government to-day must be positive, must take the initiative in an active policy of development and welfare. The trustee, in fact, must be replaced by the educator and the guardian, and the concept of trusteeship be supplemented by that of partnership.

For these and other reasons, it seems best, while perhaps retaining the mandatory principle for the existing mandated areas, to include it within a wholly new system. This system must be as comprehensively international as possible. It is no good blinking the fact that some colonial areas are by no means well administered, either in the sense of efficiency or in that of promoting the welfare of their inhabitants. The world's conscience will not long continue to tolerate any such gross inequality of standards. What is more, inefficient administration and insufficient development interfere with world prosperity. And inequality of treatment will, sooner rather than later, create a sense of political grievance. Malays, Negroes, Melanesians—all the colonial peoples are rapidly and inevitably reaching a level at which they are capable of a simple but heady brand of political thinking. In the so-called Dark Continent, for instance, fifty years ago the negro millions still lived their tribal lives as ignorant of the word *Africa* and its implications as were the vast majority of Indians a century ago of the implications of the word *India.* To-day, however, there is a rapidly growing minority who think of themselves first and foremost as Africans; and the Italian annexation of Abyssinia, together with the fact that the white men have fought two wars among themselves in the last twenty-five years, is now in the background of the native mind from the Sudan to the Cape, from Tanganyika to French West Africa. Africans can see just as far beyond their noses as other people: and inequality of treatment in neighbouring areas, perhaps more than any other type of injustice, is likely to produce a resentful and dangerous type of Africanism, in place of the healthy African patriotism and ambition which it should be the business of the colonial powers to encourage and to guide.

What system, then, should we aim at setting up? In the first place, it is desirable that the new conceptions of colonial status should be internationally expressed and publicly proclaimed. This would probably be best accomplished by the promulgation of a Colonial Charter, which would be for the colonial peoples what Magna Carta was to medieval England or the Declaration of Independence to the infant United States. Such a Charter should be jointly proclaimed by as many as possible of the United Nations; it would be difficult for any of the colonial powers to stand outside for long. It should be neither detailed nor lengthy, but need affirm only a few general principles. First, colonial dependencies are not possessions but are held in trust or guardianship. Second, the primary aim of the guardianship is to help the colonial peoples as rapidly as possible toward self-government. Thirdly, its other major aim is the development of the colonial territories, first and foremost for the benefit of their own inhabitants, but also for that of the rest of the world. Fourthly, the guardianship is to be exercised jointly by all the nations adhering to the Charter, but its administrative responsibilities are to be delegated to powers with colonial experience. Fifthly, colonial status implies no inherent or permanent inequality: no such inequality exists, and equal status and equal opportunity for all peoples and races is the goal to be realized as quickly as possible. Sixthly, all posts in the permanent colonial services, up to the highest, shall be open to the local inhabitants, subject only to selection for efficiency; and the educational system of the colonies shall have as one of its prime functions the training of men of local race for such posts. Seventhly and finally, all nations adhering to the Charter shall have equality of economic opportunity in the colonies, and also equality of all other types of opportunity, subject only to the need for maintaining efficiency of administration, and to the primacy of the claims of the native inhabitants.

The best method of implementing the Charter will probably be by a series of international conventions. The organization for handling such conventions lies ready to hand, in the shape of the International Labour Office (though in some cases other types of international instrument, such as the Congo Basin Treaty, may be preferable). The I.L.O. already has a colonial section, which would merely require strengthening. If it be asked what the conventions would cover, we can answer: forced labour, labour conditions, social security, and welfare in general, and opportunities for employment and education. The great advantage of the method is that it is a progressive one, which can contribute to a steady raising of standards in relation to changing world conditions. Its effectiveness would be increased if means were found to associate local organizations, such as agricultural co-operatives, say, or bodies concerned with social welfare, with the detailed application of the conventions to particular areas.

Secondly, even if executive responsibility is left in the hands of powers with colonial experience, their administration can be to some extent internationalized. A small proportion of technical posts should immediately be thrown open to qualified men of any nationality, and the proportion should be gradually but steadily increased. The actual selection should be left in the hands of the power concerned, for otherwise it could not well continue to assume executive responsibility. As time went on and the system proved workable, it could be extended to administrative posts as well. Meanwhile an increasing number of increasingly important posts would become filled by inhabitants of the colonies themselves.

Thus there would be parallel progress toward international government and toward self-government; and even if in some cases international government takes the lead, its share in actual administration will all the time be growing quantitatively less and that of self-government quantitatively more.

International supervision and regulation will also be needed at the outset, both to ensure proper standards and also to give some degree of responsibility to the other powers and some outlet for their natural desire to participate in colonial affairs.

This could be provided in the form of a colonial section of whatever international political organization comes into being after the war: let us call it the Colonial Commission. We need not try now to define the detailed constitution and organizational machinery of any such body. What we ought to define are its broad structure and its main functions.

Structurally, the trend of informed opinion is in favour of regional decentralization, delegating most of the work of the Commission to strong Regional Councils. These would include representatives of the colonial powers in the region, of other great powers especially interested strategically or economically, of independent nations within the region, and of the colonial peoples themselves, and perhaps also of the smaller non-colonial powers. It would be responsible, within the framework of a world authority, for general security and economic and social development within the region, not merely with regional colonial problems. It would have its own international staff of experts and advisers and, let us hope, considerable funds.

Next we come to the functions of the Colonial Commission, as delegated to the Regional Councils. One major function should be planning. A second is advice. And the third is financial help. The experience of large-scale development organizations, such as the Tennessee Valley Authority in the U. S. A., shows that a set-up of this kind, although without executive authority (the TVA has executive authority only in connection with its dams and power plants, not in matters of health, agricultural improvement, education, recreation, and so forth), can be extremely efficient in supervising and guiding development along right lines.

There are various prerequisites. The whole programme

depends on securing the co-operation of all executive organizations concerned. The regional authority must be prepared
to act as a general catalyst and as an organizer of joint action
whenever several separate organizations are concerned in a
project. In the long run, it depends also on popular understanding and backing: for this, participation by local bodies
and communities and by the agencies of education and of
public opinion is needed. Then the planning must be based
on ample research and survey: the advice must be based on
detailed field knowledge: and there must be an ample supply
of men of first-class calibre to go where the problems are.

The separate colonial powers will no doubt have their
own funds for colonial development and their own staff of
experts and travelling advisers, such as Britain, for instance,
is already building up. There should be no more difficulty in
combining these with the resources of the Colonial Commission in a common programme than there has been difficulty in pooling the resources of, say, the Land-Grant
Colleges, the State Universities, the forestry and agricultural
services of the Department of Agriculture, and the Young
Farmers' Clubs with those of the TVA in securing a sane
agricultural development in the Tennessee Valley area.

There remains the function of reviewing progress and of
detecting any failure of the colonial powers to live up to their
executive responsibilities. It might be best that detailed
review, including any inspection which might prove necessary, should be kept in the hands of the International
Labour Office, which would then report to the Colonial
Commission on any matters concerning general principles
or demanding political action, or the Regional Councils
might have their own travelling inspectorate.

I have left to the last the most urgent problem—the raising
of standards of life in the backward tropical colonies. Though
this is primarily an economic and social problem, it has its
political aspects. It concerns the political future of the
colonies themselves, since political aspirations toward self-
government must be built on the foundations of prosperity
and education. And it concerns the political future of the

advanced nations, since in the joint development by them of backward areas is to be found the only possible substitute for imperialism in the tightly-knit unit world of after the war.

Let us first try to picture more in detail some of the hard facts which are included in the phrase "tropical backwardness." It is not easy, for the life of most colonial peoples is lived on a different level of history from ours, and is measurable by quite other standards. The tropics are in large part just emerging from primitive tribal existence; at the best, they are still mainly in the barbaric phase of culture—prescientific, pre-technological. They are almost entirely lacking in the apparatus of modern civilization. The task of development is immense—nothing less than the capital equipment of the tropics for civilized living. But if we can carry it through, we shall have benefited ourselves as well as the native peoples of the colonies. While they are in their present backward state they cannot provide good markets for the manufactures of advanced countries; they cannot make any adequate contribution to the industrial and cultural life of the world; and even as a source of cheap labour they will be inefficient and unreliable so long as they remain unhealthy and uneducated. We need a complete reversal of the mercantilist policy.

Let us take a look at the extent of the job which this policy implies. In the first place, the idea of the tropics as a luxuriant region, effortlessly producing abundance and riches, is a fable. Almost the only tropical regions which are prosperous are some of those endowed with mineral wealth. Soil erosion, absence of necessary mineral salts, pests and parasites, are common. The tropics are to a large extent still physically untamed and unequipped. Railways, motor roads, ports, bridges, warehouse and storage facilities, processing plants, marketing services, dams and reservoirs, power plants, forestry, agricultural and veterinary services—in most areas these are in their infancy and must be provided on a generous scale before the colonies can take their proper place in world economy, where they can act as a stimulus rather than a drag. In addition, encouragement must be given to light and secondary industries, for only so can a reasonably balanced economy grow up in colonial areas.

But human resources are just as important as material resources. By and large the inhabitants of tropical colonies are miserably equipped with health, energy, education, and technical skill. The noble savage, the magnificent human animal endowed with the health of which civilization has robbed us degenerate whites—that is another myth. The tropical peoples as a whole are unhealthy peoples. In the tropics, vital statistics are very dubious, but we know enough to say that death- and disease-rates are of a different order of magnitude from those which applied science has made possible in the Western world. To take but a few examples: African infant mortality ranges from 1 in 4 to 1 in 2, as against the 1 in 15 to 1 in 25 of civilized countries; probably every adult negro is infested with one or more kinds of worms, usually including hookworm, and often with malaria as well; in some areas up to 90 per cent. of the population suffers from venereal disease; gross malnutrition as well as vitamin deficiency is frequent. The white man in the tropics curses the native for his laziness. But if the native were once rid of parasitic and infectious disease and given an adequate diet, he would not merely be more energetic: his entire personality would be transformed.

Improved health would provide the physiological basis for a new advance: education is needed to provide the mental basis. The tropics are as backward in education as in health. Over most of Africa, not 10 per cent. of the children ever go to any school; and not 10 per cent. of the schools are anything but the most primitive sub-elementary bush-schools, confining themselves to hymn-singing, the catechism, and the rudiments of the three R's. When the so-called primitive is given his chance, he can learn as well as anyone else. He can acquire mechanical skill, as exemplified in the workshops of the Belgian Congo; intellectual skill, as is to be seen in the Gold Coast; military proficiency, as has been demonstrated in Ethiopia during this war by the black troops from Nigeria and East Africa. For the realization of the people's latent abilities, home background and some general culture are needed as well as schools. But, given two or three generations of good education and of outlets for those who have been educated, the tropics would be as radically transformed in mind and capabilities as they would be in body and energies by proper health and diet. Tropical backwardness, economic, political, physical, and mental, is not an inescapable and permanent fact of nature; it is a temporary phenomenon which can be remedied if we are willing to make the necessary effort.

What measures should be taken to lift the tropical countries and their inhabitants out of this slough of backwardness? It is clear that the task is too large, too complex, and too long-term to be left wholly or even mainly to the free play of private initiative.

The British Government has, during the war, passed the Colonial Development and Welfare Act. This has not only increased five-fold the amounts available from central funds for colonial development, but has made social and educational improvements eligible for grants as well as purely commercial projects.

This is an important step, but it is not enough. Aid for colonial development must be on a much grander scale, and it must be in large measure international. The first prerequisite is an exhaustive survey of resources and needs, backed by adequate pure research. Anthropology, waterpower, mineral and forest resources, soils, erosion, agricultural products, transport and marketing needs, home economics, health, population trends, the prospects of export and home industries—all need to be surveyed in a much more comprehensive way than has yet been done. Lord Hailey's *African Survey* has itself stressed the need for the expansion and co-ordination of research.

Next comes the financing of development. This can be done in various ways. Colonial profits and revenues will only go a short distance. Loans and grants-in-aid, both from the separate colonial powers and from the international

Colonial Commission, will be of importance. And private finance, largely guided into desirable channels through some international investment board, can still play a major role. Already the British and American authorities are considering ways and means for setting up international finance agencies, among whose functions would be the promotion of development in backward areas.

For the actual job of carrying out development, special agencies and methods will be needed. Existing colonial governments can continue doing much valuable work. Then we may envisage the setting up of more organizations of the type of the Empire Cotton-Growing Corporation in the Sudan, where co-operatives of native producers are organized with the aid both of private finance and government aid. We shall require a careful organization of marketing agencies for all products which are regulated by international schemes of commodity control. And we shall certainly need special long-term planning and development agencies of rather new type.

One valuable suggestion, which will apply to those numerous tropical regions where all-round development is needed for a longish period before commercial profit can be expected, is to set up agencies rather of the type of the TVA, but adapted to regions of greater backwardness, and under some international control. Their function would be social as much as economic, and would involve the transformation of every aspect of life—a task which obviously requires long-term planning as well as large-scale capital investment. We may call such bodies Regional Development Agencies.

For other regions where a profitable external market is already, or will shortly be, available, a different type of body is needed, which we may christen the International Public Concern. Their shareholders should be given a minimum rate of return on their investment by international guarantee. In return for this a maximum rate should also be laid down; all profits in excess of this must be returned to the area, and a certain proportion must be set aside for social, educational, and health improvement (somewhat as with the

Miners' Welfare Fund in Britain). This compulsory plough-
ing-back of any excess profits is essential if the development
of the area is to proceed at a reasonable rate: at present there
is an undue and illegitimate drain of wealth from the backward to the advanced nations. Finally, as such concerns are
bound to exert a dominant influence on all aspects of native
life, it is essential that they should operate under welfare and
conservation regulations approved by the Colonial Commission. Existing private concerns (some of which, like the
United Africa Company, are huge and powerful bodies)
must clearly be subjected to similar regulation, social as well
as financial.

There are many other aspects of colonial development
which it would be interesting to discuss, but space forbids.
I would, however, like to mention two. First, it is very
important that there should be a well-thought-out population policy for backward areas. As health measures bear fruit,
we may expect a formidable spurt of population growth in
areas such as typical Africa; and population pressure is
one of the main causes of economic backwardness in countries like India. Thus the provision of birth-control facilities
should be a recognized part of the colonial health programme.

Finally, we must do our utmost to secure a continuity of
cultural growth, even for the most backward peoples of the
world. At present, in most areas the old tribal society and
its values and ideals are being rapidly destroyed, and nothing
solid is being put in its place. The detribalized native too
often gets the worst of both worlds, acquiring a rather
unpleasant veneer of imitation white civilization over roots
of tribal ignorance and superstition.

Is it not possible to combine the old and the new in a
better way—to graft the better aspects of modern technology
and education on to a healthy stock of native tradition and
skill? There have been some interesting experiments in this
direction, notably at Achimota College in the Gold Coast.
Already the experiment has demonstrated the immense access
of self-respect and vitality which accrues to the African
when he finds he can produce by his own efforts something

which is of high standard and useful to the community. The new policy of the Indian Bureau in the U.S.A. is bearing similar fruit. Only by such means can one encourage the native peoples to take pride in their own traditions and achievements, and enable them to make a distinctive contribution to world culture.

I can sum up the pith of the colonial problem in a brief final paragraph. This war is a symptom of a major historical transformation which will pursue its inexorable course whether we like it or not—a transformation toward a world that will be more socialized, more planned, more internationally organized than the nineteenth-century world that is fading out. But if we cannot prevent that transformation taking place, we can help to guide it. We can see that it is achieved either in a totalitarian, Hitlerian, way, or in a democratic, co-operative way. In the former case the new world order will be based on inequality and on domination by force, in the latter on equality and on mutual help. In regard to colonies, nationalist imperialism, however enlightened, was inevitably tainted with inequality, exploitation, and forcible domination. The alternative is to treat the colonial peoples as human beings like ourselves, to be guided, helped, and developed toward future political and cultural equality; the responsibility for this rests not on the few colonial powers, but jointly on all the advanced nations. Once this alternative is chosen, all else is a mere matter of machinery and will follow in due course.

RECONSTRUCTION AND PEACE:
NEEDS AND OPPORTUNITIES

Why We Should Begin to Think of Reconstruction Now

THE needs of reconstruction are the opportunities of peace. That was true in 1919, but the opportunities were missed, the needs inadequately met. After this war, we must not again lose our chance. Opportunities are rare enough in all conscience. It takes a war or a revolution to throw them up: we cannot afford to let them slip on time's turbid current.

If we are to make sure of using the opportunities for peace which this war is bringing us, we should begin our thinking and our planning now, at once. Far from it being a waste of time and energy to think about reconstruction and the final settlement now, it is the only way to make sure that we shall not miss the peace bus when it looms upon us, sudden and unexpected, round the corner of events. And just as the needs of reconstruction can be the opportunities of peace and stability in the post-reconstruction period, so the needs of war can be the opportunities of reconstruction in the post-war period. By proper care and foresight now in planning and applying various war-time measures of control, we can facilitate the urgent business of reconstructing Europe with the utmost speed as soon as the guns cease firing and the planes stop dropping bombs. The course of present events helps to determine the future. Let us always try to think two moves ahead of destiny.

The Needs of Reconstruction

We are so busy smashing up German industry, German communications, German-occupied ports, that we are only beginning to envisage the reverse problem of construction

164

that will face us and the world at large as soon as the war is
over.

We can be sure that the Nazis will fight as long as they
can. The time may come when they will know that they are
doomed, but will wish to do as much damage as possible to
their hated enemies in the process. That will mean that both
physical shortage and physical destruction will be pushed
to the limit before the war comes to its reluctant end.

Let us try to envisage the picture of destruction and want
and misery that will be Europe at the end of the war. Not
only will there have been no new building to meet the acute
demands of Europe for new and modern housing, both in its
cities and in its backward country areas, but bombing will
have destroyed a great number of existing dwellings. The
number will probably be much greater than in the devastated
areas of the last war; but in any case the destruction of
military objectives will be much higher. All over Western
and Central Europe, ports, goods and shunting yards, canals,
stores and warehouses, power-houses, gasholders, and of
course every kind of factory, both for armaments and
normal production, will have been sought out and attacked
from the air.

Besides this, normal replacements and repairs will not have
been carried out, so that a great deal of machinery will have
been worked beyond its normal life; thousands of miles of
railway track will be worn out and in urgent need of re-lay-
ing, and thousands of railway wagons on their last legs;
the world will be short of many hundreds of ships.

All in all, the longer the war continues, the more will
industrial production in Germany and German-occupied
countries be reduced to below its 1939 level.

There will be a shortage, possibly an acute shortage, of
most key raw materials, including foodstuffs, owing to our
blockade and to the diversion of foodstuffs to purposes of
armament production.

Over thousands of square miles of Europe the population,
at least the civilian population, will be hungry, and will have
been going short of vitamins and fuel-foods of various kinds

for years; and over other countries like Poland, deliberately kept by the Nazis at a lower nutritional level, not hunger but famine and starvation will be brooding.

Famine and hunger bring their own diseases, including strange psychological states where men are prone to irritable desperation. They also lessen men's resistance to infectious diseases. At the same time, misery and disorganization can hardly fail to bring about the spread of such creatures as lice and rats, which carry epidemic scourges like typhus and plague.

Just as the reserves of industrial machinery will have been depleted by excessive use, so the reserves of Europe's machinery for food-production will have been largely exhausted. Agriculture will inevitably have been misused in order to cater for immediate needs. Huge quantities of livestock which, in the light of peace-time needs, should have been kept to provide milk and wool and as breeding-stock for the next generation will have been slaughtered for their immediate value as meat; the land will have been starved of fertilizers, exploited and exhausted almost to the limit; drainage and upkeep will have fallen away to a minimum.

It will be somebody's job to see that this appalling mess is tidied up. If we win the war, then without question a great deal of the responsibility for the job will be ours. The more efficient our blockade, the hungrier the peoples of Europe will grow, the more the likelihood of epidemics will increase, and the greater will be the number of slaughtered cattle and sheep. The more factories we put out of action with our bombs, the longer it will take to produce the new machinery and rolling stock and permanent way that Europe will so gravely need. The more ports and railway junctions we smash up, the more difficult it will be to rush in the food and steel and oil for which Europe will be crying out. Let us at least see that we prepare ourselves for the task of building up as efficiently as we have carried out the terrible but necessary task of destruction.

For convenience' sake, we should distinguish two phases of reconstruction—first, the phase of making good, or

reconstruction in the strict sense, during which war damage
to the essential organs of European life is repaired; and
secondly, the phase of development, or long-term reconstruction, during which the backward areas are properly
equipped, and Europe is deliberately developed in such a
way as to prevent another recurrence of economic insecurity
and misery. Not until both are accomplished can we be said
to have reached the stage of definitive peace. Reconstruction
is insurance—involving a heavy premium to be sure, but a
premium to insure the world against chaos and bloody revolution. Development is investment—again involving heavy
expenditure, but an expenditure which is necessary to provide
the capital equipment for peace and security, for decent
standards of living, and for eventual abundance.

The Mistakes of Last Time

A very similar situation confronted the victorious Allies
at the close of the last war, though it will almost certainly
be more serious this time. I may quote from Maynard Keynes'
Economic Consequences of the Peace as to the situation at
the end of 1918. On p. 22 he writes:

> The war had so shaken this system as to endanger the
> life of Europe altogether. A great part of the Continent
> was sick and dying; its population was greatly in excess of
> the numbers for which a livelihood was available, its
> organization was destroyed, its transport system ruptured,
> and its food supplies terribly impaired.

Again on p. 212 he forecasts a possibility which has been
only too truly realized:

> Europe consists of the densest aggregation of population
> in the history of the world. . . . In relation to other
> continents Europe is not self-sufficient; in particular it
> cannot feed itself. Internally the population is not evenly
> distributed, but much of it is crowded into a relatively
> small number of dense industrial centres. This population
> secured for itself a livelihood before the War, without
> much margin of surplus, by means of a delicate and
> immensely complicated organization, of which the founda-
> tions were supported by coal, iron, transport, and an

unbroken supply of imported food and raw materials from other continents. By the destruction of this organization and the interruption of the stream of supplies, a part of this population is deprived of its means of livelihood. Emigration is not open to the redundant surplus. . . . The danger confronting us, therefore, is the rapid depression of the standard of life of the European populations to a point which will mean actual starvation for some. . . . Men will not always die quietly. For starvation, which brings to some lethargy and a helpless despair, drives other temperaments to the nervous instability of hysteria and to a mad despair. And these in their distress may overturn the remnants of organization, and submerge civilization itself in their attempts to satisfy desperately the overwhelming needs of the individual.

What were the mistakes that were made in those fatal months after the Armistice, when destiny was still plastic? Keynes, withdrawing from the Peace Conference to write his indictment of its methods and its conclusions, was able to point out most of them at the time. Others, like Harold Nicolson in his *Peace-making 1919,* have later filled in the gaps and surveyed the errors in a more general light.

This is not the place to go into detail: the post-mortem has been already conducted several times. But we may enumerate what seem to have been the major mistakes. In the first place, the peace treaty mixed the idealism of the newly founded League of Nations with the deliberately vindictive reparations clauses, with the inevitable result that the Germans, even when they were at last permitted to join the League, were constantly suspicious of its aims and methods.

Then the reparations were not only impossible to carry out, but were punitive in essence, condemning Germany (in so far as they could be and were executed) for an indefinite period to a status and standard of life inferior to that of the rest of Europe; they thus inevitably generated hatred and a desire for revenge.

The war-guilt clauses attached a moral stigma to Germany. Similarly, the moral element in the Mandate system for the ex-German colonies, however praiseworthy in certain respects, had implications as to Germany's unfitness for possessing colonies which rankled more than straightforward annexation would have done.

Meanwhile the League was set up, with its elaborate formal constitution and its paper machinery for collective security. But no real force could be quickly mobilized behind it, nor was there any directly under its control. At the same time, partly under the pressure of the multitudinous desire of the men under arms to get back to their homes and partly under the influence of high but unpractical ideology, the Allies did not march to Berlin, or by any other means bring home to the Germans as a whole the fact that they had suffered a grave military defeat. The maximum of moral turpitude was attached to Germany, coupled with the minimum of effective control, whether of Germany in particular or of European affairs in general. And this inevitably led to a movement for equality of status (which in its turn only too readily spilled over into revenge and a new bid for dominance in Europe), and to the rise of an elaborate mythology of grievance, which, coupled with the legend of a militarily undefeated Germany, gave both justification and driving force to the movement for revenge.

The next grave mistake concerned the machinery of reconstruction and relief. In the first place, there was the horrible and senseless prolongation of the food shortage in Central Europe for over six months, with great suffering to innocent children and consequently great bitterness. This is often blamed on the prolongation of the blockade. As a matter of fact, it was mainly due to the withdrawal of the United States from further participation in the elaborate and very efficient machinery of shipping and raw material control which the Allies had gradually perfected. This withdrawal, which was decided on even before the Armistice, satisfied the American desire to return to *laisser-faire*; but it did away with the only arrangements which could have ensured that the right food-stuffs and raw materials should reach the destinations where they were most needed, as quickly and as abundantly as possible. In the absence of the planned control of priorities that this would have made possible, there was much dislocation of shipping, German and Austrian tonnage could not be used to transport food to ex-enemy countries, and it was not until the summer of 1919 that the wrangling died down and proper arrangements could be made. All this not only prolonged the agony of many millions of human beings, but left behind it a sense of frustration and economic grievance which had much to do with Germany's later mood.

Another major mistake was made over the financing of reconstruction. Instead of putting all credit under some disinterested and international control, private finance was allowed to step in and make its own arrangements. Much of the vast loan provision made to Europe went to objects of quite secondary importance (such as providing amenities for German municipalities). Some of it went to individual capitalists who were neither politically nor socially responsible, nor accountable for the way it was expended. Indeed, one or two of the big German industrialists were so deluded by the fear of "Bolshevism" that they used the prosperity of which the loans had laid the foundations to give liberal help to the Nazi party. Thyssen, for instance, gave the Nazis over 5½ million pounds.

Finally, many of the loans were short-term, thus encouraging financial insecurity. One of the decisive factors in the rise of the Nazis was the withdrawal of American loans to Germany. This process started in the boom period in 1928, to provide further funds for the then profitable American pastime of gambling in securities. Then, after the crash, there was in 1930 and 1931 a much larger withdrawal of short-term loans. This included British withdrawals, which, however, constituted but a small proportion of the total. These operations were perfectly legitimate in terms of private finance: but private finance should never have been in a position to undertake them, since they caused the final wave of misery, frustration, insecurity, and disillusionment on whose crest the Nazi party rode to power. In 1928, before the first withdrawals, the Nazis had secured less than 2 per cent. of the seats in the Reichstag. After them, in 1930, the proportion jumped to 16.5 per cent. And this again was more than doubled after the second withdrawals; by July 1932 the Nazis had 35.5 per cent. of the seats.

There were also grave political mistakes. This is not the place to discuss them or their relevance to the general principles which underlie or should underlie our aims in this war. But a certain framework must be presumed. I would summarize this, as briefly as possible, as follows. We are fighting to establish a system which shall provide both freedom and security. We are fighting for the principle, which is central both to the Christian and the democratic idea, that the individual has an ultimate and irreducible value, and that the Nazi belief that the individual exists for the State is not only wicked and disastrous but scientifically untrue. As a corollary, one of our aims must be the organization of the State as an instrument of service to society, for only so, we are discovering, can we hope to provide either adequate security or adequate freedom to the individual.

Obligation to the State, as the instrument by which alone the good life can be realized, must be embodied in some comprehensive scheme of national service; but the State must assume entire responsibility for seeing that every individual citizen can reach a certain minimum standard—of health, housing, education, and enjoyment; can be sure of economic and social security at all ages; and can enjoy certain opportunities for development and self-expression.

Internationally, we are fighting against the idea of a political order in which a *Herrenvolk* dominates a number of semi-subject neighbour nations; and what we are fighting for is an organization following the general principles of the British Commonwealth of Nations, in being based on common values and common interests, but with some more definite political organization, and with specific machinery for collective security, for securing economic stability, and for promoting the development of backward areas. In passing, the relations of industrial and agricultural production will have to be carefully adjusted. To achieve permanent stability, we must envisage a quadrilateral relation between countries of different industrial types and levels. The most highly industrialized countries, like Britain and Belgium, will concentrate on specialized industry, with an agriculture supported in such a way that it can be devoted mainly to providing protective food-stuffs; countries like the U.S.A. would be exporting mainly low-grade agricultural products and heavy capital equipment; peasant regions, like South-East Europe, would concentrate on high-grade agriculture and unspecialized industry; and colonies and similar areas will furnish tropical raw materials, while making a beginning with local secondary industries.

Preparations for Relief and Order in Europe

UNRRA, the United Nations Relief and Rehabilitation Agency, has now come into being to carry out this formidable task. It is preparing the vast stores we shall need to rush into Europe as soon as the "cease fire" sounds—food and medical supplies for the human population, feeding-stuffs for the surviving livestock, seed and new breeding-stock for the depleted agriculture of our unfortunate continent. Our preparations for this need may also be desirable as war-time measures, and in addition may be of real service to the primary producing countries of the world, so many of which are cut off from their normal markets. Merely in order to keep the wheels of economic life turning in Nigeria and the Gold Coast and the Free French Colonies in West Africa during the early years of the war, we have had to buy up various crops. It was at one time proposed that these surpluses should be burnt, as had been done in peace-time with Brazil's surplus coffee: but it was speedily realized that here was a case where our present policy should be determined by our aims for the future, and that it was not only desirable but necessary, in view of the needs of reconstruction, to store the surpluses wherever possible. We bought surplus Egyptian cotton and East African sisal, the Australian and South African wool clip; we made arrangements with Australia and New Zealand to share the cost of buying, storing, and where possible processing their surpluses of food-stuffs; including meat; and we co-operated with various South American countries in solving their surplus problems, and are going to tackle the wheat surplus. A further desirable step is the processing of such materials as cannot readily be stored raw. Among the most obvious candidates for this would be various animal feeding-stuffs, meat, and dried milk.

From our step-by-step viewpoint, any such provision of storage facilities or processing plant in tropical Africa or other relatively backward areas would be a contribution to eventual economic stability and so to peace. We have begun to realize the need for spending a great deal of money on backward areas—on communications, drainage and reclamation, land betterment, ports, crop storage and marketing facilities, water storage, power projects, local secondary industries. These constitute the equipment necessary for such countries to play their full role in the world's economic life, just as up-to-date machinery is the necessary equipment of an industrial plant; and judicious investment in such equipment will pay in both cases. In the long run it will pay by raising the standard of life and the level of purchasing power in backward areas, and so stimulating a high level of world trade and production all round.

Medical supplies will need medical men to administer them and to remedy the ill-health and probably epidemic disease which will be spread across Europe. Here again preparatory action is being taken, but more could be done, especially to enlist the services of refugee doctors from Europe.

Nor will doctors and public health officials be the only trained men needed. Agricultural experts of all kinds, welfare workers, skilled administrators for the territories over which we shall have to exert a temporary control—the call on their services will be as urgent, and they too should be organized beforehand.

Relief organization and expert service can only function under some orderly and efficient system of authority; but Europe immediately after the war is not likely to be very orderly, and in many parts it may well be that no stable authority will exist, or none to which one would wish to delegate the supervision of relief.

Thus, one of the great needs of Central Europe during the reconstruction period will be order and authority; and this too must be planned beforehand. The Nazis have taken so much trouble to stamp out every independent organization in Germany that there is little likelihood of any nucleus surviving a German collapse, stable enough to serve immediately as the basis for a new Government. If so, a Germany that was left to itself would become the scene of appalling acts of revenge by the anti-Nazis, of a bloody and confused turmoil of miniature civil wars. Nor must we forget the surrounding nations, especially those whom Germany has so viciously and brutally oppressed. If Germany collapses thoroughly, hundreds of thousands of German throats will be in danger of being cut by Poles, by Czechs, by Dutchmen, Norwegians, and Danes, by Belgians and Frenchmen, by other Germans. The Allied Military Government in Italy is an experiment paving the way for interim bodies to be set up under military control in other parts of Europe as they are liberated, and the Inter-Allied Advisory Council for Italy will doubtless set the pattern for similar political control agencies for Europe as a whole.

In any case, it would seem essential that this country should continue during reconstruction that role as leader of the forces of freedom which it has found the strength to assume during the war. After the conclusion of hostilities there will be, as there was in 1919, a clamour and pressure from weary, bored, and impatient men to get out of uniform and back to their homes and their work. We must be careful not to allow it to override all other interests. It will be necessary for us to keep on the continent of Europe a considerable force for a number of years after the war. Our force should be supplemented with contingents from the Dominions and other countries, including, one may hope, the U.S.A., even if these be sometimes no more than token forces. But the main contingent in Western Europe will probably have to be British, just as the main lines of policy must be Anglo-American, Britain acting as the Western European agent, so to speak, of the three-power kernel of the United Nations partnership. Another reason for keeping a strong force on the Continent is to prevent whatever constructive peace-making machinery is set up from being confronted with *faits accomplis* by irresponsible national armies, as happened to the Versailles Conference in 1919.

These are all in a sense technical details. The essential is to prepare for this role now. And the preparation must be largely psychological: the sense of mission and leadership which began to be so manifest in the nation in the late summer of 1940, when we realized that we were the sole hope of the world against the Nazi menace, must be reinforced and projected outwards on to Europe and onwards into the future. One form which the necessary psychological preparation should take is that of political education in the Army. We shall not be able to educate Central Europe if we do not first educate the instrument of that education—the Army. Here ABCA and the general scheme of Army Education have already accomplished a great deal, while intensive courses have been instituted for special administrative personnel.

The Reconstruction Commission

After the relief of actual hunger and disease, and the maintenance of order, the most urgent need will be the repair of the physical machinery of living. The organs of production, of distribution, and of human existence, must be patched up, set going, improved.

Many of the raw materials needed by Europe must be imported. If we are to obtain a speedy and orderly recovery, the importation of these materials must be planned according to a strict scheme of priorities. Otherwise luxuries will often be imported instead of necessities, and relatively prosperous areas will have their demands met before those which, just because they need more, can afford to bid less in the open market.

Thus the planning of a priority scheme will involve not only the retention of the systems of raw material and shipping control now exerted by our Ministries of Economic Warfare and of War Transport in conjunction with Washington, but also the setting up of some new system for allocating credits and raw materials where they are most needed.

Everything points to the absolute necessity of entrusting the whole business of European relief and reconstruction to a single, official body: *Reconstruction Commission* will serve as a provisional title. It must obviously operate on behalf of Governments—the Governments of Britain, the U.S.S.R., and the United States, and of as many of the Dominions, the Allied countries, and the neutral nations as are willing to adhere: but Britain, the U.S.S.R., and the U.S.A. must be the major partners, since they will be the main guarantors of order.

The first task of the Reconstruction Commission will be to make a rough survey of the needs to be met, and the means available to meet them. Throughout, the classical approach through finance must be rejected, and the problem worked out in the concrete terms of needs, materials, and man-hours. This is the way the problems of war are faced, and finance then has to adjust itself to these basic realities. We have found how relatively easily it can adjust itself within the single nation; the lend-lease principle shows how it can adjust itself to these same realities in international relations. If we face the no less urgent problems of reconstruction in the same way, it will adjust itself no less easily to them. Finance is not and must not again be allowed to become primary: needs and productive capacity are primary.

This means that the Reconstruction Commission must have complete control of all credits for reconstruction purposes. In other words, the British and American Governments, together with any others that choose to join in, should make the reconstruction of Europe a priority claim on their planned investment policy. Their return will be long-term and indirect, in increased trade and stability rather than in money; but it will be none the less valuable for that. What is more important, these same Governments, which will be in control of the major part of the world's raw materials and shipping, will be rationing these commodities and conveniences, through the Reconstruction Commission, in such a way as to give a high priority to the re-establishment of the European standard of living. They will be doing this even at some expense to their own standard of living, which will not rise at such a rate as it might otherwise have done.

If once these principles are agreed on, then several extremely interesting possibilities are opened up, of using reconstruction as a stepping-stone to peaceful stability. One concerns the restriction of national sovereignty; a second concerns the role of the German people in post-war Europe; and a third concerns the finding of the people and organizations to whom the government of Germany may safely be entrusted.

Nationalism and Industry

Everybody knows by now that unrestricted national sovereignty is the central problem of international politics to-day, and perhaps the main cause of the failure of the League of Nations. The insistence of the small states of Europe on their sovereign right to neutrality (which in turn was the result of the larger nations' insistence on their sovereign rights to independent action, at the cost of international co-operation for pooled security) was a major cause of Hitler's extraordinary successes in the spring of 1940.

The sovereign right of nations to do as they like about their internal affairs allowed the Nazis to upset the whole civilized world by the persecution of Jews and liberal-minded "Aryans."

In some of its aspects, the doctrine of unrestricted national sovereignty is quite fictitious, in others it is the rationalization of crude power-politics; in both cases, it is mischievous and leads to the undermining of political security.

Clearly something must be done about it. But what? Frontal attacks have failed. May it not be best to consider indirect attack? Consider the nature of national power at the present time. It depends, in the first instance, on enormous supplies of armaments; and modern armaments are elaborate and costly, demanding all the resources of mass production and precision industry. War to-day is a technological business. It cannot be waged unless backed by high industrial potential. This is only another way of saying that modern war must be total war; it demands total control of economic resources and production. National sovereignty is not truly unrestricted if it has not that economic control.

Now it so happens that the industrial resources of Europe, notably as regards the basic heavy industries and their ancillary transport mechanisms, have been laid out by nature in a way which by no means coincides with the set-up of national boundaries or indeed with ethnic or language groups. (See map.)

The outstanding case of what we may call a transnational natural region—an industrial area cutting right across national boundaries—is the great concentration of industry in North-Western Europe. This includes the Ruhr and the Saar in Germany, Luxemburg, Lorraine, parts of north-eastern France and central Belgium, and a sector in Holland, with their coal, lignite and iron ore, not to mention a certain amount of salt and limestone, their steel, copper, and zinc works, their admirable rail communications in all directions, their great rivers and canals and ports.

This region is largely interdependent—long before the war the coal of the French-Belgian-Ruhr coalfield was used to smelt the iron ore of Luxemburg and Lorraine, while the German and the Dutch canals and rivers and the railways of the north German plain are indispensable for transport; and this natural interdependence had been used as the basis for functional agreements between different national components of the industries concerned. The steel works and other industrial concerns agreed to take so much coal from the mines, and the chemical industries take the by-products from various works; the whole was largely tied into a single industrial unit.

Another striking example is the Silesian triangle, with its

MAP SHOWING NATIONAL BOUNDARIES AND TRANSNATIONAL
INDUSTRIAL AREAS OF WESTERN EUROPE

1. France, Belgium, Holland, Germany, Luxemburg: Iron, coal, heavy industry, heavy chemicals.
2. Germany, Czechoslovakia: Brown coal, heavy industry, chemicals, textiles.
3. Czechoslovakia, Germany, Poland: Iron, coal, chemicals, oil, timber, heavy industry, metallurgy.
4. France, Germany, Switzerland: Iron, coal, steel, engineering, chemicals.
5. Switzerland, France, Italy, Austria: Electric power, electro-chemical industries, engineering precision industry.
6. France, Spain: Mining, metallurgy, electric power, heavy industry.
7. Norway, Sweden, Finland (a large but natural area): Iron, copper, nickel, gold, arsenic, etc., metallurgy, chemicals.
8. Belgium, Holland, Denmark, Norway, Sweden, Germany: Shipbuilding, ports.
9. Britain, Norway: Whaling.
10. Central Germany (see text).
11. Balkan Nations: Mining, oil, etc. (as yet largely undeveloped).

coal, iron, lead, zinc, salt, oil, timber, and natural gas, an eminently natural region from the standpoint of industrial resources, but politically overlapping Germany, Czechoslovakia, and Poland.

Other transnational regions are the slopes of the Erzgebirge, with chemical, steel, engineering, and armament works, but divided between Germany and Czechoslovakia; the Upper Rhine, overlapping Germany, France, and northern Switzerland; and the western Alps and the adjacent low country, focused on the recent growth of hydro-electric power, and divided between France, Switzerland, Austria, and Italy. Of rather a different type is the coast from northern Belgium through Holland and north-west Germany to Denmark and southern Scandinavia, a potential functional unit concerned with shipbuilding and ports.

Let us look at the matter from the opposite angle—that of the national units concerned and their sovereignty in economic affairs. Obviously Germany is here the test case. It was through its capacity to mobilize its economic resources as a unit behind its war machine that Germany became the major threat to European peace. We are sometimes told that Germany's industrial system is a fact of nature which we must accept, and that Germany is inevitably destined to be the industrial kernel of Central Europe and the dominating factor in its economic life. In point of fact, Germany is, industrially speaking, a highly unnatural unit.

We have just seen that the largest centre of German industry is interlocked with France, Luxemburg, Belgium, and Holland, its Silesian component with Poland and Czechoslovakia, its Saxon component with Czechoslovakia, its south-western component with France and Switzerland, and that its main shipbuilding area could properly and profitably be integrated with those of Holland, Belgium, and Denmark.

In fact, the only important industrial region which is confined exclusively to Germany is that of the central German plain, from Hanover and Cassel to Leipzig and Berlin.

We must further remember that certain aspects of German industry are artificial conditions of German nationalism. This is partly true of the core region just mentioned, since the natural resources of this area are scanty, consisting merely of a moderate supply of lignite and coal, and its industries have largely grown up around the national railway system. Further, in this and other regions, numerous *Ersatz* and synthetic industries have been deliberately built up in the pursuit of autarkic self-sufficiency, many of which (as well as some others) have been maintained at an unnaturally high level by means of tariffs or subsidies; and during the present war yet others have been moved far to the eastward to avoid the attentions of our bombers. In a rationally organized Europe, these factors also in German industrial dominance would disappear.

The same is true, to a greater or lesser extent, of most other industrial sections of Europe. We have seen how the north-eastern and south-eastern components of French industry fall into transnational regions. There is a good deal to be said for integrating the coal-mines of the Pas de Calais and the adjacent northern French textile industry with the industries (apart from shipbuilding) of Holland and western Belgium in a single transnational unit. And if it were desired, France's southern industrial area round Toulouse could be functionally linked with the Catalonian industrial area centred on Barcelona, and with the mineral regions of the Basque country and the Asturias. Brittany and south-western England have many common interests. The Norwegian whaling industries could be integrated with those of Britain, while in mining and metallurgy Norway, Sweden, and Finland constitute an obvious natural unit.

Among the more powerful countries, only Russia, and to a lesser but considerable extent Britain, remain as political units whose industry does not naturally fall apart into a number of transnational groupings. However, Russia is rather an Empire than a nation, and Britain's position is complicated by its extreme dependence on imports.

Transnational Industry, Reconstruction, and Security

Is it not possible to take advantage of these convenient facts of nature to promote a transnational structure for

European heavy industry? Such a structure would not be anti-national, but it would be anti-nationalist.

We have already made the point that a powerful Reconstruction Commission, backed by international authority, and armed with large powers of control, is necessary if reconstruction is to be either speedy or efficient. Such a body would also be in a position to impose almost any structure it liked upon European industry. It should be charged with the duty of developing a non-national structure wherever possible. This would be its long-range aim, behind its immediate and primary duty of seeing that reconstruction was carried out with maximum speed and efficiency.

It would first make its own survey and decide provisionally on the number and boundaries of the "industrial regions" which it proposed to recognize. Next, the Commission would get in touch with leading industrialists in each of these regions, and would request them to organize the industrial enterprises of their region in Regional Industrial Associations, with which alone the Reconstruction Commission would be willing to deal. None of the raw materials which were being internationally controlled would be directly available to single factories or single undertakings, still less to national combines operating in several industrial regions. The same would hold for credits, with the additional point that no credits would be allocated to banks, whether local or national or international, for disposal as they wished. Credits and raw materials alike would be allocated through Regional Associations only. What is more, they would be allocated in relation to a carefully worked out scheme for the economic rehabilitation of Europe as a whole, and the Regional Associations would be obliged to follow the lines of this scheme in using the materials and credits they received. The plan might, for instance, insist that so much of the industrial capacity of the Silesian industrial region should be devoted to turning out steel rails, so much to new machine tools, so much to lorries, so much to chemicals, while a certain amount of machinery and possibly entire factories (arma-

ments factories, for instance) might have to be written off
as so much surplus war material.

Any objections of the Regional Association would be carefully considered, but in the long run the Commission would
have the whip hand through its power of cutting off supplies.
No undertaking could afford to stay outside its proper
Regional Association, for it would receive no credits and no
raw materials for its industrial plants. Neither could any
firm or combine, or any national portion of a transnational
region, embark on a line of its own counter to the policy
approved for the Regional Association as a whole, for as soon
as the Reconstruction Commission became cognizant of this,
it would be able to cut off the proportion of supplies due
to the offending unit, which would then be helpless.

This is of importance both for reconstruction and for
peace. It is important for reconstruction since it provides a
means by which the Reconstruction Commission's plan for
priorities can be enforced. A particular firm might think
that it could make higher profits by turning over from the
production of, say, commercial lorries to luxury automobiles;
a particular nation might wish to see its citizens made happy
by an immediate increase in consumption goods, rather than
forced to remain on a Spartan regime while industry was
kept busy turning out whatever is most urgently needed for
reconstruction. Neither the profit motive nor political considerations should be allowed to interfere with the job of
re-equipping Europe: and here is a method for seeing that
no such interference shall take place.

The same applies to rearmament. We may be sure that if
the Germans are beaten, they will be prohibited from building warplanes, tanks, or heavy guns. Given the powers of
inspection that will obviously be needed, the Reconstruction
Commission could at once nip in the bud any attempt at
infringing this ban by withdrawing the material and financial
basis for its realization. Sanctions, in fact, become automatic.
The machinery by means of which they may be enforced is
already working, and the authority capable of enforcing
them is there, and in a position to make an immediately

executed decision. This is in strong contrast with sanctions under the League. There, political discussions between numerous powers were needed before any decision could be taken, and the machinery of enforcement had to be built up *ad hoc* on each occasion.

It is thus clear that the Reconstruction Commission would become involved in matters of high politics, and it is therefore necessary to consider the international and political backing which it ought to possess. For some time after the end of hostilities, Britain and the Dominions, together with the U.S.S.R. and the U.S.A., will presumably have to undertake, jointly, the main responsibility for order, relief, and reconstruction in Europe. However, this grouping of nations should obviously regard itself merely as a nucleus out of which some more international political organization might develop. It is outside the scope of this essay to discuss the steps by which this might be accomplished, but presumably invitations to participate would be extended as soon as possible to other democracies and friendly neutrals, and steps taken to hammer out the lines of a more elaborate and more comprehensive system later.

Some central international body must exist, and the experience of the League seems to indicate that the method of sending Prime Ministers or Foreign Ministers to represent their nations is not satisfactory. They will be tempted to act in a hurry; and in any case, a man whose main job is to serve the interests of his particular nation can hardly be expected every few months to step out of the train prepared to undertake the quite different job of serving Europe. This, however, is not the place to discuss political reconstruction. But a word of warning is not out of place. In 1919, Versailles staked too much on the political principle of self-determination, and grossly neglected the economic bases of security and order. Let us, after this war, beware that we do not stake too much on economic planning, vital though it be, and unduly neglect political organization. National feelings are basic facts; and cultural self-determination and patriotism are valuable and must play a vital role in a co-operative European organism.

The German Role in Europe

We come next to the bearings of a sane reconstruction policy on the future of the German people in Europe. There are two facts of this question. The first concerns the problems of reparation (I deliberately refrain from using the term in the plural and with a capital letter—Reparations—because of its association with the disastrous Reparations policy imposed in 1919). The second concerns our picture of the role that we envisage the Germans playing, during the next phase of history, in the economic and cultural life of Europe.

To this latter problem there are a certain limited number of possible solutions. Some impossible solutions have also been proposed, such as the extermination of the German "race": but at our present stage of civilization it is unthinkable to attempt the extermination of 60 (or 80) millions of human beings. Granted that the Nazis appear to be attempting something of the sort, though on a smaller scale, with the Poles, that is no reason for our even considering such a course of action as within the bounds of possibility.

Permanent foreign occupation, under which the Germans are to be forced to work as they are directed, is another impossible solution. It remains as true to-day as in the time of Napoleon that you cannot sit on bayonets.

Among the possible solutions are, first, the forcible political partition of Germany, with the assignment of as much as possible of the fragmented body of the Reich to other national units. Most of those who know Germany regard this type of solution (apart from the restoration of Austrian independence) as a very poor and inevitably temporary one. It thinks solely in terms of the balance of power; and by forcibly dividing the Reich it would provide a real and ready-made grievance, and at once set up the reattainment of unity as the one goal and ardent hope of all politically minded Germans.

In point of fact, no solution is realistic which makes boundaries, or the balance of power along nationalistic lines, its primary consideration. Even regional federations are, by themselves, a wholly unsatisfactory solution. We must think in terms of Europe, and of the role of the German people within the European whole, not in terms of Germany and its relations with other separate powers or groups of powers.

Along these lines, two kinds of solution have been proposed. One advocates the necessity of keeping the Germans in a position of inferiority, permanently or at least indefinitely, and subject to political restrictions, to inspection, to lower economic standards, which are not imposed upon the rest of the European peoples. The other insists that there must be no such discrimination against the Germans, since this will inevitably unite them behind a movement to free themselves of the discriminations. Get rid of the Nazis, it is urged, and then invite the remaining Germans to free and equal co-operation.

Each of these solutions is the logical outcome of an irrefutable proposition. Proposition number one asserts that Germany has been so consistently aggressive over so long a period, and has so deliberately provoked three major and a couple of minor wars in less than a century, that the German nation simply cannot be trusted again. Proposition number two, on the other hand, maintains that the refusal to trust the German people, with its inevitable consequence of discrimination against them, contains the seed out of which another German war cannot help but grow.

These two propositions are at first sight irreconcilable. But reflection shows that they are only irreconcilable if we wish to apply definitive solutions immediately, once and for all. That too is unrealistic. In human history, time is of the essence of the contract, for it provides the possibility of change. No solution can be fitted complete, like a suit of clothes. History is a creative process in time; and the only possible solution for the German problem is one which shall limit and as far as possible prescribe the course of German history after the war so as to avoid the recrudescence of the German threat to security, while at the same time holding out the eventual goal of honourable and equal co-operation in world affairs, political as well as economic.

In spite of all efforts in certain quarters to establish the contrary, we must distinguish between the German people and the ruling gang which has been able to seize power in Germany. It is perfectly true that this gang has succeeded in imposing its ideas on a considerable minority of the German people, and that this constitutes a grave problem of re-education. On the other hand, it is merely erroneous to state that the German people differ inherently and biologically from the rest of Europe in being incurably savage and aggressive.

Next, we must distinguish between the claims of Germany and those of Europe and the world. Europe and the world have a right to impose restraints and restrictions which will render a repetition of German aggression impossible or unlikely. We must not sentimentalize over these restraints, but must be prepared to live up to our beliefs that war can be prevented, and to use the power that we shall have at the end of hostilities in order to prevent it. On the other hand, as human beings, the Germans have certain essential claims. We must think of these claims less in terms of the claims of Germany and more in terms of the claims of the German people. A reasonable claim would seem to be this —that individual Germans, once the reconstruction period is over, shall have a status in Europe, and an opportunity for a healthy and useful existence, which shall be as good as, though certainly no better than, those open to the individual Englishman, Belgian, Czech, or Pole. The claims of Europe demand that we and all other European nations shall aim at setting up a system which offers reasonable social and economic security to European men and women, and also reasonable opportunities of leading an interesting and useful life; one, further, in which the possibility of oppression by minority groups shall be removed, and in which military and economic power, both actual and potential, shall be

decentralized and distributed so as to make the threat of
military aggression by Germany or any other single nation
as unreal as the threat of an organized uprising in York-
shire or Cornwall.

Our New European Order

Looked at from another angle, we may contrast Hitler's
plan for a New Order (however badly it has by now gone
astray) with the type of New Order which we would hope
to see established. Hitler set out to establish a German
hegemony in Europe on the basis of the myth of German
superiority. The Germans were to be a *Herrenvolk*, running
the rest of Europe for Europe's benefit, but more especially
their own. Economically and industrially, his "new order"
deliberately set out to amplify certain inequalities already
apparent in Europe by rigging the position in Germany's
favour, notably by bringing the key points under German
control and restricting the key industries, so far as possible,
to Germany itself; this was to be accomplished even if it
meant lowered standards of living for all other European
peoples, who would come to occupy the role of colonies in
relation to the metropolitan German power.

Any New Order which we could think of establishing,
however, should be based politically, so far as possible, on
the principle which we have developed to such an extent
in the British Commonwealth; namely, of free and equal
units, co-operating on the basis of consent and of agreement
on common values (though some more centralized control
will be needed in Europe than in the British Commonwealth). Economically our interest would lie in decentraliz-
ing industry, in building up industrial organizations on
transnational lines, and in developing the more backward
regions of Europe as quickly as possible so as to extend
purchasing power and, at the same time, to remove those
patches of economic weakness which, in the past, have led
to economic frustration and political unrest.

It would be a great mistake, in the opinion of those who
have studied the British Commonwealth most thoroughly,

to attempt, in building up a new political framework in Europe, to start with any form of written constitution. This would mean throwing overboard our own tested methods in favour of an attempt at logical completeness, which will, almost certainly, defeat its own ends. All that will be necessary is some form of economic control such as could readily grow out of the work of the Reconstruction Commission, some form of security control for Europe, which could readily grow out of the series of armed contingents now operating as our Allies, some European Council or Assembly, some adequate common fund available for various international purchases and for the developing of backward areas, and some international Staff College. A central broadcasting service and organizations for leisure, education, and social services would also be highly desirable, if not immediately essential.

The first formal step toward the setting up of our New Order was the declaration at the gathering of representatives of all the Allied nations at St. James's Palace in the late spring of 1941; and since then much necessary spadework has been done.

Meanwhile, our experience in the Commonwealth indicates another new approach. In the past, wars have always been followed by a single Peace Conference, which attempted to lay down at one stroke conditions for the ensuing period of peace. In the British Commonwealth, on the other hand, there has never been any attempt to lay down its organization definitively at any one time, but we have preferred to adjust its growth to changing conditions by means of a series of Imperial Conferences. May it not be worth while to try the same method for Europe, holding a series of conferences during and after the reconstruction period? This would provide a much better permanent method for securing peaceful change than a single conference, or than the setting up at one stroke of elaborate machinery, such as was established under the League of Nations. It would also facilitate the difficult transition from reconstruction to definitive peace.

One important factor in that transition will be the discovery of those elements of the German people to whom power will eventually have to be entrusted, their testing in positions of progressively greater responsibility, the gradual delegation to them of increasing doses of independence. When Germany is beaten, it seems safe to prophesy that the internal collapse will be much more complete than in 1918. The Nazis have so successfully destroyed all independent organizations that no nuclei of effective political crystallization remain, and the result of a Nazi collapse will be best described as a national deliquescence. That means that, if we wish to avoid a blood-bath on a large scale, German territory must be effectively controlled. The bitter pill of military occupation should be partially sugared by making the armed force carry out police duties and assist to the utmost in the work of relief. The presence of the armed force will facilitate the activities of the Reconstruction Commission, and it will be accompanied by administrators carefully trained beforehand for their difficult task. But from the outset Germans must be found to operate the details of local administration. This should not be too difficult. The Nazified professional organizations of Germany, and the Nazi party itself, are only in part composed of true believers. There is a considerable proportion of non-Nazis and even of anti-Nazis who joined the various organizations as a matter of self-preservation. Through some appropriate machinery of tribunals the body politic can be purged of its Nazi elements, and men found to whom the detailed business of local administration can be entrusted. Under the supervision of the Allied civil administrators, these German local government bodies can be tested out in practice. As time passes, some elements will be rejected, others chosen to be entrusted with greater responsibilities. Independence, in fact, will be gradually delegated, beginning on the local level, and passing through various stages with fewer and fewer reserved powers, until—whether in five, or ten, or twenty years—Germany, like other European countries, will be granted the fullest possible independence (analogous to Dominion status in the British Commonwealth) within the European Commonwealth of free and equal nations.

Reparation, not Reparations

There remains the problem of reparation. Reparations, in the sense of cash payments by the defeated aggressor for war damage inflicted on other countries, speedily revealed themselves in practice as the economic absurdity and impossibility which economists like Keynes proclaimed them to be when they were first mooted. In so far as they are purely punitive, they are politically inept, and they also delay general economic recovery. Yet both justice and expediency demand that aggressors should make some reparation for their guilt and for the damage they have caused.

A controlled reconstruction provides the possibility of reconciling moral justice with economic law and European welfare. For some time after the war, every country in Europe, as well as many outside it, will have to make sacrifices if the reconstruction of that continent is to take place with the greatest possible speed. They will have to continue on a lower level of consumption in order to provide Europe with new capital equipment. Europe, in fact, will be faced with a situation very like that of the U.S.S.R. during its first five-year plan, when the standard of living had to remain low so as to provide the country with the agencies of heavy industrial production. Reconstruction economy will differ from war economy in the constructive nature of its aims, with the slogan of capital goods before butter instead of guns before butter, and also, let us hope, in not being quantitatively so drastic, but it will resemble war economy qualitatively in its immediate effects, in discouraging spending and in restricting consumption.

With the control of priorities in the hands of a Reconstruction Commission, the Germans could be compelled to make reparation by requiring them to supply a larger proportion of the equipment needed to restore economic life in the countries they had overrun, and so keeping them longer on a low-consumption economy. Germany is now going short of consumption goods because she has been exporting bombs and crashed Messerschmitts to Britain, tanks to Russia and Libya, and sunk troopships to the bottom of the sea; she must continue to go short of consumption goods because she will be exporting industrial machinery and steel and locomotives and precision instruments and housing equipment to Belgium and Holland, Poland and Jugoslavia.

The Germans will not go short of the foodstuffs necessary for full health, or the materials required to reconstruct their own heavy industry and transport on a peace footing; but they will not be allowed to produce any variety of consumption or luxury goods, nor will they be in a position to import them, until they have liquidated a reasonable amount of their debt to Europe by aiding the reconstruction of their victims. Reparation will be made by delaying the re-establishment of peace-time standards in Germany, but not by preventing that re-establishment, nor by penalizing the German people in their health or by refusing to allow them to co-operate with the rest of Europe in its common task and its eventual common prosperity.

Commodity Control and World Prosperity

So far we have worked forwards from the needs of a devastated Europe to draw the outline of a positive reconstruction agency which in its turn might pave the way for more permanent international organizations. It is now time to reverse our procedure and look ahead into the post-reconstruction period to see what organizations will be necessary to prevent the world from sliding back into chaos. Here also the organized international control of raw materials and other commodities turns out to be important. It could be important not only as an agency of stability, but as one of promoting international unity and potential security. In addition, the features of a good system of commodity control are much easier to discern than those of any international political organization of the future.

Many, however, still cherish rooted objections to any form of commodity control. They say that it is inevitably a form of monopoly, that it always operates to restrict output and to raise prices, and puts more power in the hands of producers. For their benefit, it will be necessary to discuss control schemes in general.

First, then, we must distinguish the actual past from the possible future, and be careful not to confuse practicability with desirability. It is clear that international control schemes are practicable. They have steadily increased in number, and this growth has been a natural result of recent economic tendencies. A few were in operation before 1914; the dislocation caused by the last war, coupled with the governmental control exercised during it, brought a number of others into existence, and a further and even greater stimulus was given by the Great Depression. Not all have worked equally well, but their working has been gradually improved. Their chief defects have been, first, that they were operated in the interest of producers. Even when governments have helped in their organization, this has generally been due to a desire to help their own producers (or even a particular section of them). The control schemes have thus been producer-minded, and this has had various disadvantages. Inefficient and high-cost producers have often been saved from disaster, with consequent failure to lower prices; restriction of output and the maintenance of an unduly high level of profit (as with tin) has often been the main aim, instead of a somewhat lower rate of profit, but on an increased production; consumer interests have usually not been considered, and have often actually suffered; dangerous monopoly power has sometimes been established, notably where demand is inelastic. The difficulty of bringing all producers into a scheme has meant that important groups often stay outside, and cash in on the benefits in good times without having made any sacrifices when times were hard. Finally, much too little attempt has been made to undertake market surveys and to encourage consumer demand.

In spite of all these disadvantages, however, control schemes have brought various benefits. The greatest of these is some measure of stability. The price of rubber per pound varied between 4s. and 2½d. between 1925 and 1932: it was worth while for the world to face some restriction of output and to bear some increase in average price in order to get rid of such economic chaos. Control by restriction of output is also justified as a method of meeting obviously temporary declines in demand. Control by price stabilization and by buffer pools are deliberate attempts to increase stability by smoothing out the effects of the trade cycle with its recurrence of booms and slumps: the trouble is that producer-mindedness tends to stabilize prices upwards.

Furthermore, the disadvantages are not inevitable. The world production of aluminum, of which nearly three-quarters was under a control scheme, increased by nearly 75 per cent. in the eight years after 1921. Nickel was very largely controlled, yet in 1937 the price was reduced by 10 per cent. and its consumption increased by 20 per cent. and continued to expand later. Under the tea scheme, which controlled some four-fifths of the world's production, a Tea Development Board was set up to improve marketing facilities and increase consumption, while a reasonable price policy was pursued: as a result, consumption increased by more than 30 per cent. in the one year 1939. The Brazilian coffee control, though mismanaged in various ways, at least kept the industry alive and saved Brazil from a major economic disaster. Finally, under the International Rubber Committee, consumer interests, notably those of the U.S.A., which produces no rubber at all, were represented on the Committee, though in an advisory capacity only.

From another angle, the chief disadvantage of control schemes in the past was that they were politically irresponsible, or even that through them producer interests tended to dominate the political sphere of action, alike on its domestic and foreign sides, so as often to override both consumer and national interests. Control schemes are clearly practicable. The answer to the question whether they are desirable or not depends on whether they can be subordinated to political power so as to become its instruments.

Let us try to envisage how this might be accomplished. As soon as possible, Britain, the Dominions, and the U.S.A., perhaps in conjunction with the U.S.S.R., would jointly announce that they intended to form associations of their own producers of a limited number of key raw materials, and that they invited producers from other countries to adhere, through the intermediary of their Governments. The arrangement would begin functioning at once, and would be intended to continue after the war.

Each commodity (or group of cognate commodities) would have its own control board, and all the separate controls would be the organs of a single Raw Materials Union. On each board, in addition to producer representatives there would be representatives of governments, in their consumer as well as their producer capacity. All actual transactions would be in the hands of the separate control boards. But the general terms of reference would be laid down by the central Union itself—price policy, conditions for re-export or compulsory barter transactions, the terms on which outsiders might participate, and so forth. The general lines of policy in relation to the balance between the various materials controlled would of course also be the affair of the Union; and it would in its turn be subordinate to the central political authority in matters where economic policy has broad political repercussions.

As the scheme began to prove its worth, further controls for other commodities would be set up, until the great bulk of the raw materials of the countries adhering to the Union would be organized and controlled in this way. In addition, associations of wholesalers and of manufacturers would be invited to adhere as consuming members. In the world's political and economic danger spots, special distributing mechanisms would be required to obviate attempts at illicit rearmament and nationalist autarky: to this point we shall return.

Some advantage should accrue to the nations and the pro-

ducer associations which adhere to the Union. Apart from
the political advantage of increased security, and the politico-
economic advantage of increased stability, commercial advantage must be knitted into the scheme. This could readily
be provided in some form of discount or dividend available
to members but not to non-members. In addition, each Control will have the duty of building up central funds above a
certain minimum amount. Out of this, marketing surveys
and campaigns for increasing consumption will be financed,
and a reserve retained as an insurance fund against any
losses incurred by members as a result of control being
utilized as a form of economic sanctions. Much of this,
however, is technical detail, with which we need not here
concern ourselves.

Commodity Control and Political Security

How will such a scheme work and what good will it do?
We must at the outset distinguish between two quite
separate functions of such an organization, the one positive
and economic, concerned with increasing welfare, the other
negative and political, concerned with enforcing a form of
sanctions. These two functions should be kept as separate
as possible, and the responsibility for deciding to withdraw
supplies from an offending nation should rest in other hands
from those which are concerned with the day-to-day production and distribution of raw material. If not, there will be
the danger of the defeated countries feeling that raw material
control in its positive aspect is itself being made to serve a
political purpose, and becoming resentful and suspicious
of the whole scheme.

This could be obviated in some such way as the following.
Responsibility for seeing that no illicit rearmament or other
breaches of international covenants were occurring would
be undertaken by some body—call it the International
Technical Commission—which would be wholly separate
from the Raw Materials Union, and responsible solely to
whatever central political authority is erected on the international plane.

If the Technical Commission discovers any breach of

covenant—and the placing of obstacles in the way of the Commission's work would itself constitute a breach—it would report to the political authority, preferably perhaps through its judicial organ.

Instead of the all-or-none method envisaged under the League of Nations, with no intermediate stage between normal trade and complete sanctions, it would be better to follow the best modern penal procedure, and grade the penalties in stages. For a first infringement (remembering, as we in this country know to our cost, that it takes time to rearm effectively), a warning from the judicial authority would be sufficient. If this warning were not heeded within a definite period, limited sanctions could be applied. By this is meant the withholding of a few raw materials which are essential for armaments, such as nickel and molybdenum. This could be done without the gross dislocation of world trade which inevitably follows from complete economic sanctions, and any loss to individual producer associations could be met from the insurance fund set up by the particular control scheme involved. This measure of limited sanctions might properly continue, like the first warning, to be automatic.

If the warning were again disregarded, the Technical Commission would again report, via the judicial authority, to the central political authority. It should then be obligatory on this body, after verification of the fact, to order the Raw Materials Union to set full sanctions into force. The offending nation would thus be deprived of all the raw materials controlled by the Union.

The duty of applying sanctions when instructed to do so by the competent judicial or political authority should be written into the charter or constitution of the Raw Materials Union and its constituent Controls.

Security could also be provided by utilizing the international control of raw materials to promote a non-national grouping of industry in the world's danger-spots, notably Western and Central Europe. These regions would be specially scheduled as occasion demanded, and in these Scheduled Areas it would be laid down that raw materials would be supplied by the Union only to approved industrial organizations. Organizations would not be recognized for this purpose unless they were natural groupings; purely national organizations would not be approved (see p. 147 *seq.*).

It is, of course, obvious that the security problem must be tackled from the military end also. This might be done by means of an International Force which alone would be empowered to employ the essential instruments of modern war—tanks, military planes and heavy artillery; or it might be achieved through internationalized arms depots and training grounds, at which national contingents could be trained in the use of these prohibited armaments (prohibited, that is, to separate national states), and from which a supply of armaments could be speedily rushed to any threatened area. In point of fact, it would seem preferable to employ a combination of the two methods: as men trained in an international cadre and imbued with an international spirit became available in larger numbers, the relative importance of the International Force would be increased.

If we envisage some such definite set-up for the next phase of world history, it is easy to see how it could be made to grow naturally and integrally out of the arrangements designed to tide over the period of reconstruction. There is no point in trying to anticipate the detailed course of the future and the precise timing by which the organs of the provisional set-up would become transformed or absorbed into the larger and definitive scheme. As long as both immediate urgencies and long-term desirabilities are kept in mind from the outset, the transition from war to reconstruction and from reconstruction to true peace can be made without cataclysmic reversals of policy and with a minimum of dislocation.

Conclusion

We have ranged widely over a number of fields. It will be as well to end by recapitulating some of the desirable results which a sane reconstruction policy could produce.

By the device of recurrent conferences, the dangers of hasty decisions by a single Peace Conference could be avoided, and efficient machinery set up for securing peaceful change.

By placing all relief and reconstruction under an official Reconstruction Commission, priorities could be enforced which would raise the standard of life in Europe as rapidly as possible, help to develop backward areas, and impose an industrial structure which would cut across national boundaries and place grave difficulties in the way of economic autarky. At the same time the Commission would be in a position to enforce a substitute for reparations on the Germans by insisting that they should be responsible for producing a larger share of the equipment needed for reconstructing European industry and communications; this would merely delay their attainment of a peace-time standard of consumption, while neither starving them nor discriminating permanently against them.

By organizing a general scheme of raw material control with adequate consumer representation, and by utilizing the Reconstruction Commission as its European agency, reconstruction could be linked with development. Economic instability could be minimized, consumption gradually increased, and an automatic and efficient mechanism for economic sanctions provided which would effectively prevent illicit rearmament.

In many fields, preparation for reconstruction ought to be pressed forward as rapidly as possible. Surplus stocks are already being accumulated and in some cases processed; men are being selected for the difficult job of administering large parts of central Europe before it can safely be entrusted to administer its own affairs; and a European Advisory Council has been brought into being. But the foundations of the future Raw Materials Union should be laid, and also those of the future super-national political authority.

If reconstruction in the narrow sense must be a first charge after the war, this must be followed by a period of development, during which a further large slice of the world's resources must be invested in the capital equipment of backward areas. This is a pre-requisite for a permanent increase in the standard of living, and an insurance against slumps and mass unemployment.

An improved balance between different types and levels of agriculture and industry in different areas is essential for stability and increasing prosperity; in particular, it is necessary if the world's relatively backward areas are to free their present excess of agricultural population for other occupations, such as building, local industry, etc., and so raise their level of consumption.

For all this, which amounts to saying for the future peace and security of the world, planned reconstruction is essential.

"RACE" IN EUROPE

Nature and Origin of the Group-sentiment

OF ALL appeals to which human beings respond, few are
as powerful as that of tribal, or—in a more advanced
stage—of national feeling. Such sentiment is at the basis
of life in the modern State. It is doubtless founded upon
some form of the herd impulse, which receives satisfaction
in social animals through the presence of other animals
like themselves. In Man, however, this impulse, like other
so-called "instincts," is not simple and straightforward in
operation. The likenesses upon which this "consciousness
of kind" is based are inborn in animals: but in Man they
are very largely acquired, being the product of experience
and social factors.

Very many human activities, aspirations, and emotions
have contributed, either naturally or artificially, to build
up the great synthesis that we term a "nation"; language,
religion, art, law, even food, gesture, table manners, clothing,
and sport all play their part. So also does the sentiment
of kinship, for the family has extended some of its age-old
glamour to that wholly different and much newer aggregate, the national unit. I would stress the contrast between
family and nation, since the family is an ancient and
biological factor, while the nation-state is a modern conception and product, the result of certain peculiar social and
economic circumstances. The family has been produced
by Nature, the nation by Man himself.

Before the Renaissance, that is to say before the fifteenth
century, nations or national states in our sense of the word
did not exist, though there were composite human aggregates related to the tribes of an earlier cultural stage. For
the moment we will call the sentiment which holds tribes
and nations together "group-sentiment." To call it "racial"
is to beg a very important question which it is the purpose

of this essay to discuss. It is, however, clear that even in the pre-Renaissance stage group-sentiment was a complex thing, certain elements being derived from the idea of kinship, certain others from local feeling, from economic necessity, from history, from custom, or from religion.

The transference of the idea of kinship to the "group-sentiment" of nations has been fateful for our civilization. For while the idea of kinship is one of the most primitive emotional stimuli, the sentiment which it arouses is also one of the most enduring. It is for this reason that the authors of moral and legal codes have frequently found it necessary to protect the State against aspects of group-sentiment which induced hostility to foreign elements. The Bible is full of allusions to such checks. "The stranger that dwelleth with you shall be unto you as one born among you, and thou shalt love him as thyself; for ye were strangers in the land of Egypt: I am the Lord your God" (Leviticus xix. 34). "One ordinance shall be both for you of the congregation, and also for the stranger that sojourneth with you, an ordinance for ever in your generations: as ye are, so shall the stranger be before the Lord." (Numbers xv. 15). One of the most gracious parables of Jesus is devoted to the discussion of who is our neighbour (Luke x. 25-37), and the very basis of Christianity is the proclamation "There is neither Jew nor Greek, there is neither bond nor free: for ye are all one in Christ Jesus" (Galatians iii. 28).

Throughout the history of civilization the establishment and regulation of group-sentiment among those who are held together mainly by political bonds has been one of the chief aims of statecraft. To achieve this the idea of kinship has been pressed into ever wider service. It has been expanded beyond the family, to embrace the tribe, then the loosely knit federation of tribes, and the yet more extensive aggregate, the nation.

The Brotherhood of Mankind

When religions and philosophies have claimed and empires have sought to be universal, the idea of kinship has been extended beyond the limits of the nation-state. Prelates have been the shepherds of many flocks, and commonwealths have become families of nations. In all ages law, reason, and religion alike have laid emphasis on the brotherhood of all mankind. It was an ancient philosopher-poet who said, "I am a man, and nothing that is human do I deem alien from myself"; and a murderer who yet earlier asked, "Am I my brother's keeper?"

But the common elements that all men share have been especially the theme of the great spiritual leaders. Malachi's question "Have we not all one Father? Hath not one God created us?", the beautiful treatise on the love of God as inseparable from the love of our fellow-men, known as the *First Epistle General of John,* and St. Paul's assertion, "He hath made of one blood all nations of men for to dwell on all the face of the earth," have all been echoed by a myriad voices. The community of mankind is a sentiment which has particularly appealed to teachers. "The same sky covers us all, the same sun and stars revolve about us, and light us all in turn," said the great Czech educator Comenius.

Of all studies the most universal is that which we call science, and with its advent in the seventeenth century the unity of mankind became especially emphasized. Such was the principle which the French scientist and philosopher Pascal detected in the continuity of research in the sciences: "The whole succession of men through the ages should be considered as one man, ever living and always learning."

The Idea of Nationality

Mankind, however, has shown itself to be still unprepared to accept the idea of universal human brotherhood, and has often denied it most loudly when maintaining the universal fatherhood of God. Tribal, religious, and national sentiment have, time and again, overruled the sentiment for humanity. The idea of nationality has yielded as fruit that patriotism which has proved itself one of the strongest forces known to history, second perhaps only to religion. It is hardly necessary to emphasize the part played by patriotic sentiment

in the moulding of Europe. The passionate desire for freedom from foreign domination—which we may note is very
far from the desire for freedom itself, with which it is often
confused—was one of the preponderating political factors
of the nineteenth century. In Germany it broke the power
of Napoleon and later created an empire; it freed Italy from
the rule of Austria and made her a nation; it drove the Turk
almost out of Europe and stimulated nationalist sentiments
among the Greeks and among all the peoples of the Balkans.
It has also been the main idea in the formation of the
"succession states" since the War of 1914-18.

All the movements toward national unity that were so
characteristic of the nineteenth century present certain
features in common. Among these we would note especially
the rise of a myth, so similar in all these cases that we must
suppose that it is a natural way of thinking for peoples in
like circumstances. Among all the newer and almost all
the older nationalities a state of freedom from external
political domination has been fictitiously supposed to have
existed in the past and has been associated with a hypothetical ancient unity, itself considered as derived from an
imaginary common inheritance. The implications of this
unity are usually left vague. A "nation" has been cynically
but not inaptly defined as "a society united by a common
error as to its origin and a common aversion to its neighbours."

The economic movements of the nineteenth century gave
rise to unparalleled social and political dislocations. The
resulting conflicts have by some been interpreted as originat-
ing from an incompatibility of "racial" elements in the populations involved. But such incompatibility, if it be a reality,
must have existed for many centuries in the populations
before these disturbances declared themselves. Such explanations therefore inevitably lead to an inquiry as to the extent
to which the claims to "racial unity," which are involved in
recent nationalist controversy, have a basis in reality.

A further question necessarily arises in this connection.
Even if we assume that for any given national unit it were

possible to establish a specific physical type—which it is not—would there be any evidence for the view that it were best that this type should be fostered and its survival encouraged to the exclusion of all other types? In coming to a conclusion we· must remember that every people has ascribed to itself special powers and aptitudes. Such claims may, at times, assume the most ridiculous forms. There is not one but a multitude of "chosen peoples." Some of the most sweeping claims made for the British, by Kipling for instance, are closely similar to the claims made for the tribes of Israel by the authors of certain Biblical books.

> Truly ye come of The Blood; slower to bless than to ban,
> Little used to lie down at the bidding of any man.

>> There's but one task for all,
>> One life for each to give,
>> What stands if Freedom fall?
>> Who dies if England live?

With *The White Man's Burden* may be compared the forty-ninth chapter of the book of Isaiah:

> The Lord hath called me from the womb. . . . And he said unto me, Thou art my servant, O Israel, in whom I will be glorified. . . . It is a light thing that thou shouldest . . . raise up the tribes of Jacob and restore the preserved of Israel: I will also give thee for a light to the Gentiles, that thou mayest be my salvation unto the end of the earth. . . . That thou mayest say to the prisoners, Go forth; to them that are in darkness, Shew yourselves!

When, too, we read in Madison Grant's *The Passing of the Great Race* that the greatest and most masterful personalities have been of Nordic type, we can make a shrewd guess at its author's general appearance! A flaw in his line of thought is that the very same claims are made by many groups that are by no means predominantly Nordic. Passages claiming leadership of the world can, in fact, be elicited in abundance from French, German, Italian, Russian, and American literature, to say nothing of the literatures of smaller groups. Nations, races, tribes, societies, classes, families—each and all claim for themselves their own peculiar, real, or imaginary excellences. This is a common human foible, but there are times and circumstances when it may become an epidemic and devastating disease.

The Meaning of "Race"

The term "race" is freely employed in many kinds of literature, but investigation of the use of the word soon reveals that no exact meaning can be attached to it. The word "race" is of Hebrew or Arabic origin, and entered the Western languages late. It was originally used to denote descendants of a single sire, especially of animals. Later in English and French it became applied to human beings, as in the phrase "the race of Abraham" in Foxe's *Book of Martyrs* (1570 edition, the first occurrence in this sense in English) or in a spiritual sense,—e.g. the "race of Satan" in Milton's *Paradise Lost*. The word was not employed in the Authorized Version of the Bible, where it is represented by the words "seed" or "generation."

The word "race" soon acquired a vagueness that it has never since lost. This vagueness has given the word a special popularity with a group of writers who deal with scientific themes, though they themselves are without adequate scientific equipment. From such writers it has descended to the literature of more violent nationalism.

It is instructive to look up the word *race* in a good dictionary. The vagueness of its usage will at once become apparent. *The Concise Oxford Dictionary* defines "race" in general as:

> "Group of persons or animals or plants connected by common descent, posterity *of* (person), house, family, tribe or nation regarded as of common stock, distinct ethnical stock (*the Caucasian, Mongolian,* &c., *r.*), genus or species or breed or variety of animals or plants, any great division of living creatures (*the human, feathered, four-footed, finny,* &c., *r.*); descent, kindred (*of noble, Oriental,* &c., *r.; separate in language & r.*); class of persons &c. with some common feature (*the r. of poets, dandies,* &c.)."

A word is often none the worse for being inexact in its usage; many words indeed are valuable for this very reason. But it is necessary, in dealing with scientific subjects, to distinguish carefully between the terms that we use in an exact sense and those which are valuable for their very vagueness. The word "race," if it is to be used at all, should find its place in the latter class.

It has frequently been asserted that "race" is of the essence of nationality, and sometimes "race" and "nation" have been used as almost interchangeable terms. So far has this gone that many nationals, if questioned, would reply that their compatriots were all of one "race," with a proportion, more or less insignificant, of "aliens," who, by some means or other, have acquired their national status. A very little reflection and knowledge will show that this view is untenable. The belief, however, survives in many quarters where it should have become extinct, sometimes with the idea of "stock" substituted for "race." Our statesmen, who should know better, often speak of the "British race," the "German race," the "Anglo-Saxon race," the "Jewish race," etc. Such phrases are devoid of any scientific significance. The speakers should usually substitute some such word as "people" or "group" for the word "race" if they desire to convey any meaning—and if they do not wish to play into the hands of Hitler and those who think like him.

It was a remarkable consequence of the Great War that, perhaps for the first time in history, peace treaties were directed toward the revision of the political map on lines which aim at having a basis in so-called "ethnic realities." For this purpose the "racial" argument was constantly put forward in terms of what, in the current phase of the time, was called "self-determination," with occasionally some regard for the rights of the so-called "racial" (usually linguistic or cultural) minorities.

In the discussion which accompanied the settlement of the peace treaties there was inevitably much confusion of thought in regard to these so-called "racial questions." As an illustration of the lengths to which such confusion of thought may go, it may be mentioned that in the discussion on the Polish Corridor it was even suggested as a means of finding the "racial" affinities of the inhabitants of the area involved, that the question might be settled by consulting the voting lists of the last election!

"Race" and "Blood"

Associated with the vague idea of "race" is the idea, almost equally vague, of "blood." The use of this word as equivalent to "relationship" is itself based on an elementary biological error. In fact there is no continuity of blood between the parent and offspring, for no drop of blood passes from the mother to the child in her womb. The misconception is very ancient and is encountered among many peoples on a low cultural level. This false conception gained scientific currency from a mistake of Aristotle, who held that the monthly periods, which do not appear during pregnancy, contribute to the substance of the child's body (Aristotle, *De Generatione Animalium*, I, § 20). The curious reader will find Aristotle's error repeated in a work in the Apocrypha, *The Wisdom of Solomon* (vii. 2). The modern knowledge of the physiology and anatomy of pregnancy disposes completely of any idea of a "blood-tie" or of "common blood" in its literal sense. Such blood is not "thicker than water." On the contrary, it is as tenuous as a ghost. It is non-existent. It is a phantasm of the mind.

But quite apart from this venerable misconception, and the widespread misunderstandings that arise from it, it is evident that the actual physical kinship, which is frequently claimed as "race feeling," must be fictitious. In many cases it is, in fact, demonstrably false even in the very simple and lowly forms of social organization. To speak of "kinship" or "common blood" for the populations of our great complex modern social systems is to talk mere nonsense.

We may take a familiar example of a lowly social organization from the Scottish clans. These, in theory, were local aggregates of families connected by kinship and each bound thereby to their chief. As an historical fact, however, these local units included settlers who came from other clans.

This mixture of relationships would naturally, in time of crisis, entail a divided allegiance. Such a danger was overcome by the enforced adoption of the clan name. Thus when the MacGregors became a broken clan and the use of the name was forbidden, its members averted the evil consequences of their outlawry by adhesion to other clans. Thus Rob Roy, the famous outlaw and chief of the Gregors, adopted his mother's name of Campbell, and so became an adherent of the Duke of Argyll.

Similarly in Ireland there was a system of wholesale inclusion of entire classes of strangers or slaves with their descendants into the clan or into its minor division, the sept. Those so adopted regularly and as a matter of course took the tribal name. In the exceedingly ancient "Brehon Laws," which go back at least to the eighth century, there are regulations for the adoption of new families into the clan and even for the amalgamation of clans. Kinship, or rather what was treated as kinship, could thus actually be acquired. It could even be bought. A number of legends of early Greece and Rome tell of similar clan fusions. Adoption into the tribe thus constantly becomes a fictitious blood-tie, and among many peoples of lower culture the ceremony of adoption is accompanied by actual physical interchange of blood. Many analogies in more advanced cultural units suggest themselves.

If a Scottish or Irish clan is of "mixed blood," what likelihood is there of purity of descent among the millions that make up the population of any great modern nation? How can there be an "Anglo-Saxon race," a "German race," a "French race," and still less a "Latin race," or an "Aryan race"? Historically, all the great modern nations are well known to be conglomerations and amalgamations of many tribes and of many waves of immigration throughout the long periods of time that make up their history. This may be well seen in southern France, where in Provence the Greek colonies of Marseilles and elsewhere became, at a very early date, integral parts of the population of Gaul. More familiar examples are to be found in the population of the British Isles, which has been made up from scores of waves of immigrants from the third millennium B.C. until the present time. Britain has thus been a melting-pot for five thousand years. Among the more modern waves was that of the Huguenot refugees, who fled from France to the eastern counties of England, and formed 5 per cent. of the population of London after the Revocation of the Edict of Nantes, and the Flemish settlers who came at a somewhat earlier date to South Wales. Both have long ceased to be separate groups, and those who number Huguenots and Flemings among their ancestors cannot be distinguished among the extremely complex mixture which forms the population of the country. In particular it may be stated that, from the earliest prehistoric times to our own, the wealthy and densely settled south-eastern part of England has been the recipient of wave on wave of immigration from the Continent. The existence of anything that can be called a "race" under such conditions is mere fantasy.

The special form of group-sentiment that we call "nationality," when submitted to analysis, thus proves to be based on something much broader but less definable than physical kinship. The occupation of a country within definite geographical boundaries, climatic conditions inducing a definite mode of life, traditions that gradually come to be shared in common, social institutions and organizations, common religious practices, even common trades or occupations—these are among the innumerable factors which have contributed in greater or less degree to the formation of national sentiment. Of very great importance is common language, strengthened by belief in a fictitious "blood-tie."

But among all the sentiments that nurture feelings of group unity, greater even than the imaginary tie of physical or even of historic relationship, is the reaction against outside interference. That, more than anything else, has fostered the development of group-consciousness. Pressure from without is probably the largest single factor in the process of national evolution.

"National Types"

It may, perhaps, be claimed that, even admitting the incorporation into the nation of many individuals of "alien blood," it is nevertheless possible to recognize and differentiate the true "stock" of a nation from the foreign. It is sometimes urged that the original stock represents the true national type, British, French, Italian, German, and the like, and that the members of that stock may readily be distinguished from the others. The use of the word or the idea of "stock" in this connection introduces a biological fallacy which we must briefly discuss.

Certainly, well-marked differences of "national type" are recognized in popular judgment—we all know the comic-paper caricature of the Frenchman, the German, etc.—but it is very remarkable how personal and variable are such judgments. Thus our German neighbours have ascribed to themselves a Teutonic type that is fair, long-headed, tall, slender, unemotional, brave, straightforward, gentle, and virile. Let us make a composite picture of a typical Teuton from the most prominent of the exponents of this view. Let him be physically as blond and mentally as unemotional as Hitler, physically as long-headed and mentally as direct as Rosenberg, as tall and truthful as Goebbels, as slender and gentle as Goering, and as manly and straightforward as Streicher. How much would he resemble the German ideal?

As for those so-called "national types" that travellers and others claim to distinguish, we may say at once that individuals vary enormously in the results of their observations. To some resemblances, to others differences, make the stronger appeal. Between two observers attention will tend to be directed to entirely different characters in the same population. Furthermore, a general conclusion as to the character of any given population will depend on how far the material examined is what statisticians call a "true random sample."

A traveller who lands at Liverpool and carefully explores

the neighbourhood of the great industrial area by which that port is surrounded, would form a very different view of the bearing, the habits, the interests, the speech, in fine, of the general appearance of the population of England, from one who landed at Southampton and investigated agricultural Hampshire. Both would obtain different results from one who landed in London, and all three from the painstaking investigator who undertook a tour of observation from Land's End to John o' Groats. Observations in Normandy or in Bayonne will give a very different impression of the French from those made in Provence, while a superficial anthropological observer from Mars who had landed in certain corners of North Wales might, for a time, easily imagine himself among a Mediterranean people, and even in some spots among a people of an older, "palaeolithic" type. Samples of the mixed population of the United States, formed from peoples of the most varied origin, might give an even more distorted impression of the general social and material conditions of its inhabitants, if the observations were confined to the east side of New York, to the Scandinavian belt of the Middle West, to the Creole population of New Orleans, or to the country districts of New England.

When, in fact, the differences which go to make up these commonly accepted distinctions between "racial stocks" and nationalities are more strictly examined, it will be found that there is very little in them that has any close relation to the physical characters by which "race" in the biological sense can be distinguished. It is more than probable that, so far as European populations are concerned, nothing in the nature of "pure race" in the biological sense has had any real existence for many centuries or even millennia. Whether it has ever had, since the days when man first became man, is a problem which is still unsolved.

Nationality depends on Cultural, not Biological, Characteristics

In considering the characters of different nationalities it will generally be found that the distinctive qualities upon which stress is laid are cultural rather than physical, and when physical, they are very often physical characters that have been produced or influenced by climatic and cultural conditions. Stature is certainly in part a function of environment. Pigmentation—fairness or darkness—unless submitted to scientific record and analysis, is illusory. How many Englishmen could give an accurate estimate of the percentage of dark-complexioned or of short people in England?—which is in fact a country whose inhabitants are more often dark than fair, more often short than tall. Expression must obviously be determined largely by the content and habit of thought. Men's faces have, stamped upon them, the marks of their prevalent emotions and of those subjects on which they most often and most deeply think.

In point of actual fact, the most crucial factors on which most observers' judgment will depend will be dress and behaviour. In dress, the use, degree, and contrast of colour at once attract the eye. In behaviour, facial expression, gesture, and speech attract much attention. These, however, are cultural factors, the results of fashion, imitation, and education. It is true that attitude and movement and the use of the voice have physical bases. But it is, nevertheless, certain that in virtue of their patent transmission by imitation they must be regarded as mainly dependent upon a cultural inheritance. It is interesting to note that in Hitler's book *Mein Kampf* his "racial" characterizations and differentiations, more especially of the Jews, are based not on any biological concept of physical descent—as to the essential nature and meaning of which he exhibits complete ignorance —but almost entirely on social and cultural elements.

The Myth of an "Ayran Race"

Apart from these general considerations, certain fallacies of unscientific "racial" conceptions, and in particular the myth of an "Aryan race," call for separate discussion.

In 1848 the young German scholar Friedrich Max Müller (1823-1900) settled in Oxford, where he remained for the rest of his life. The high character and great literary and philological gifts of Max Müller are well known. About 1853 he introduced into English usage the unlucky term *Aryan*,[1] as applied to a large group of languages. His use of this Sanskrit word contains in itself two assumptions— one linguistic, that the Indo-Persian sub-group of languages is older or more primitive than any of its relatives; the other geographical, that the cradle of the common ancestor of these languages was the Ariana of the ancients, in Central Asia. Of these the first is now known to be certainly erroneous and the second now regarded as probably erroneous. Nevertheless, around each of these two assumptions a whole library of literature has arisen.

Moreover, Max Müller threw another apple of discord. He introduced a proposition which is demonstrably false. He spoke not only of a definite Aryan language and its descendants, but also of a corresponding "Aryan race." The idea was rapidly taken up both in Germany and in England. It affected to some extent a certain number of the nationalist, historical and romantic writers, none of whom had any ethnological training. It was given especial currency by the French author de Gobineau. Of the English group it will be enough to recall some of the ablest: Thomas Carlyle (1795-1881), J. A. Froude (1818-94), Charles Kingsley (1819-75), and J. R. Green (1837-83). What these men have written on the subject has been cast by historians into the limbo of discarded and discredited theories.

In England and America the phrase "Aryan race" has quite ceased to be used by writers with scientific knowledge, though it appears occasionally in political and propagandist literature. A Foreign Secretary recently blundered into using it. In Germany the idea of an "Aryan" race received no more scientific support than in England. Nevertheless, it found able and very persistent literary advocates who made it appear very flattering to local vanity. It therefore steadily spread, fostered by special conditions.

Max Müller himself was later convinced by scientific

[1] The word *Aryan* was first used quite correctly by Sir William Jones (1746-94) as a name for the speakers of a group of Indian languages.

friends of the enormity of his error and he did his very best
to make amends. Thus in 1888 he wrote:

> I have declared again and again that if I say Aryas,
> I mean neither blood nor bones, nor hair, nor skull; I
> mean simply those who speak an Aryan language. . . .
> When I speak of them I commit myself to no anatomical
> characteristics. The blue-eyed and fair-haired Scandina-
> vians may have been conquerors or conquered. They may
> have adopted the language of their darker lords or vice-
> versa. . . . To me an ethnologist who speaks of Aryan
> race, Aryan blood, Aryan eyes and hair, is as great a
> sinner as a linguist who speaks of a dolichocephalic dic-
> tionary or a brachycephalic grammar.[1]

Max Müller frequently repeated his protest, but alas!
"the evil that man do lives after them, the good is oft interred
with their bones." Who does not wish to have had noble
ancestors? The belief in an "Aryan" race had become accepted by philologists, who knew nothing of science—and
the word was freely used by writers who claimed to treat
of science though they had no technical training and no
clear idea of the biological meaning to be attached to the
word "race." The influence of the untenable idea of an
"Aryan race" vitiates all German writings on anthropology
which are now allowed to appear. If the term "Aryan" is
given a racial meaning at all, it should be applied to that
tribal unit, whatever it was, that first *spoke a language*
distinguishable as Aryan. Of the physical characters of that
hypothetical unit it is the simple truth to say that we
know nothing whatever. As regards the locality where this
language was first spoken, the only tolerably certain statement that can be made is that it was somewhere in Asia and
was not in Europe. It is thus absurd to distinguish between
"non-Aryans" and "Europeans."

There is no need to trace in detail the history of the
Aryan controversy. It will be enough to say that while the
Germans claimed that these mythical Aryans were tall, fair,
and long-headed—the hypothetical ancestors of hypothetical

[1] Max Müller, *Biographies of Words and the Home of the
Aryas*, London, 1888, p. 120.

early Teutons—the French claimed that the Aryan language and the Aryan civilization came into Europe with the Alpines (Eurasiatics), who are of medium build, rather dark, and broad-headed. The decipherment of the language of the very "Jewish"-looking Hittites—which was certainly Aryan—and the discovery of certain Aryan languages in North-West India throws a new complexion on the whole question of the origin of the Aryan languages.

Both the German and the French views cannot be entirely true, but both may be partially or entirely erroneous. In so far as the cultural origins of our civilization can be associated with any particular physical type, it must be linked neither with the Nordic nor the Eurasiatic, but rather with the Mediterranean. As regards the general physical measurements of the existing population of central Europe, the prevailing physical type is Eurasiatic rather than either Nordic or Mediterranean.

The Jews

A consideration of this "Aryan fallacy" leads us to two so-called "race problems" which are of immediate political importance—the Nordic and the Jewish. Beginning with the latter, we find that the Jewish problem is far less a "racial" than a cultural one. Jews are no more a distinct sharply marked "race" than are German or English. The Jews of the Bible were of mixed descent. During their dispersal they have interbred with the surrounding populations, so that a number of hereditary elements derived from the immigrant Jews are scattered through the general population, and the Jewish communities have come to resemble the local population in many particulars. In this way Jews of Africa, of Eastern Europe, of Spain and Portugal, and so on, have become markedly different from each other in physical type. What they have preserved and transmitted is not "racial qualities" but religious and social traditions. Jews do not constitute a race, but a society with a strong religious basis and peculiar historic traditions, parts of which society have been forced by segregation and external pressure into forming a pseudo-national group. Biologically it is almost as illegitimate to speak of a "Jewish race" as of an "Aryan race."

The Nordic Theory

The Nordic theory, which is a development of the "Aryan fallacy," is in another category. Instead of ascribing racial qualities to a group which is to-day held together on a cultural basis, it takes a hypothetical past "race," ascribes to it a number of valuable qualities, notably initiative and leadership, and then, whenever it finds such qualities in the mixed national groups, ascribes them to the Nordic elements in the population. It then proceeds farther and sets up, as a national ideal, a return to purity of stock of a Nordic "race" the very existence of which is unproved and probably unprovable.

The real source of all these modern ideas of the innate inferiority of certain "races" is the work of the French Count Joseph de Gobineau *Essai sur l'inégalité des races humaines* (1853-5). This book is essentially a plea for "national" history. He advocated especially the superiority of the so-called "Aryan races" over others. The idea was carried to the most ridiculous lengths in the work of his countryman Lapouge, *L'Aryen* (1899), in which the "Aryans" were identified with the "Nordic race." This ridiculous Nordic-Aryan theory, launched by French writers, was eagerly developed in Germany and linked with anti-Jewish propaganda. In the beginning of the present century the East Prussian Gustav Kossinna took up the idea, applied it to prehistoric archaeology, and claimed to make German pre-history—to use his own words—"a pre-eminently national science." His naïve object was to show that throughout the prehistoric ages advances in culture had been entirely due to peoples whom he identified with the Nordic, Germanic, or "Aryan" peoples, these terms being regarded as interchangeable, though including not merely Germans but also Scandinavians. The "Aryan" cradle was conveniently located in the North European forest about the Baltic and North Sea coasts.

This theory is scientifically quite untenable on many

grounds. Thus, to take a single point, the earliest of the rough stone monuments (of which Stonehenge is a late and highly developed example, c. 1700-1600 B.C.) go back, even in England, at least as far as 3000 B.C. The culture that they represent spread from the Mediterranean to the Iberian peninsula and thence through France into Britain and beyond to north Germany and Scandinavia. Yet these monuments, involving high enterprise, considered design, and complex social organization, were produced by a people devoid of metal implements and quite certainly not of "Nordic" origin. The skulls from the early English burials associated with these monuments are, in fact, usually stated to be of "Mediterranean" type.

Nevertheless, the Nordic theory speedily became very popular in Germany. It made a special appeal to national vanity and was made the basis of propaganda in the pseudo-scientific writings of the Germanized Englishman Houston Stewart Chamberlain and others in Germany, and of Madison Grant and others in America. Hitler—himself anything but Nordic—is completely obsessed by this fantastic theory. Among the absurdities connected with the development of the theory it is perhaps sufficient to mention that Jesus Christ and Dante have been turned into "good Teutons" by German writers. The "Nordic theory" has had a very great effect, not only in serving as a basis for the "Aryan" and anti-Jewish doctrines upon which the Nazi regime is now being conducted, but also as the inspiring influence in a great deal of political agitation which claimed superiority for the "Nordic" in the discussion of legislation determining the recent revision of the immigration laws in the United States.

The facts of the case are as follows. The "Nordic race," like other human races, has no present existence. Its former existence, like that of all "pure races," is hypothetical. There does, however, exist a "Nordic type." This occurs with only a moderate degree of mixture in certain limited areas of Scandinavia, and is also to be found, though very much mixed with other types (so that all intermediates and recombinations occur), in Northern Europe from Britain to Russia, with pockets here and there in other countries. On

various grounds we can be reasonably sure that this distribution is the result of the invasion of Europe by a group largely
composed of men of this type—perhaps in the degree of
purity in which the type is now found in limited areas of
Scandinavia. This group in its original form was probably
the nearest approach to a "Nordic race." It is not certain
where it originated or when its important migration took
place. Several authorities believe that it come originally
from the steppes of southern Russia.

The contentions which ascribe to the "Nordic race" most
of the great advances of mankind during recorded history
appear to be based on nothing more serious than self-interest
and wish-fulfilment. In the first place, it is quite certain
that the great steps in civilization, when man learned to
plough, to write, to build stone houses, to transport his
goods in wheeled vehicles, were first taken in the Near
East, by peoples who by no stretch of imagination could be
called Nordic, but who seem in point of fact to have con-
sisted largely of men of the dark, "Mediterranean" type.
Secondly, it is true that great advances in civilization have
sometimes been observed in history when invaders of a
relatively light-skinned type have irrupted into countries
populated by other groups—notably in Greece, though
here round-headed as well as long-headed elements were
included in the invaders. But, in such cases, both types
appear to have made their contribution, and the result can
best be ascribed to the vivifying effects of mixture and
culture-contact. Indeed, where the Nordic type is most
prevalent, in Scandinavia, there is no evidence of any
ancient civilization having been attained at all comparable
to that of the Near East, North Africa, India, China, the
Mediterranean, or the Aegean. In more modern times the
greatest achievements of civilization have occurred in regions
of the greatest mixtures of types—Italy, France, Britain,
and Germany, to mention only four nations. In all countries
of "mixed races" it is rare to find pure Nordic types. The
great bulk of the population will contain hereditary elements
derived from many original sources. In the highly complex
populations of Britain or Germany the pure Nordic type,

if it ever existed, is quite irrecoverable, for the population as a whole is an inextricable mixture. The Nordic type may be held up as an object of policy or propaganda, but this ideal is genetically quite unattainable, and will not affect the biological realities of the situation.

Furthermore, when we look into the facts of history, we find it far from true that men of pure or even approximately Nordic type, have been the great leaders of thought or action. The great explorers of Britain displayed initiative, but hardly one of them was physically of Nordic type: the majority of the most celebrated Germans, including Goethe, Beethoven, and Kant, were medium or round-headed, not long-headed as the Nordic type should be. Napoleon, Shakespeare, Einstein, Galileo—a dozen great names spring to mind which in themselves should be enough to disperse the Nordic myth. The word *myth* is used advisedly, since this belief frequently plays a semi-religious role, as basis for a creed of passionate racialism.

"Race-mixture" is Beneficial

From what has been said, it will be clear that "race-mixture" has in the past been beneficial. The British contain strong Nordic and Eurasiatic elements, with a definite admixture of Mediterranean types. In the Germans there is a very large Eurasiatic element which includes the Slavonic, while hereditary elements from the Mongoloid peoples have crept in via Russia. Jews entered Germany in the first Christian centuries—long before many of the German tribes had emerged from what is now Russia—and it is quite possible that every man who to-day calls himself a German had some Jewish ancestors. In France the population is largely Alpine, especially in the centre, but there is a strong Nordic admixture in the north and a prevailing Mediterranean element in the south. The Jews are of mixed origin, and have steadily been growing more mixed. America is proverbially a melting-pot. The Japanese are also a mixture of several ethnic types. India is as much a product of repeated immigration as Britain, and so on throughout the peoples of the earth.

In Germany to-day, in order to establish "Aryan blood," a man must present a pedigree clear of "non-Ayran," i.e. Jewish, elements for several generations back. The enormous number of cases in which one parent or grandparent or great-grandparent of the most thoroughly "German" citizens has proved to be Jewish shows how impossible it is to secure a "pure Nordic stock." Once more, indeed, the social and cultural plane is the more important. Germany has benefited a great deal from her Jewish elements—we need only think of Heine, Haber, Mendelssohn, Einstein. But during the economic depression the competition of Jews in the professions, in finance, and in retail trade was proving embarrassing, and in the revolution it was convenient to treat the Jews as a collective scapegoat, who could be blamed for mistakes, and on whom might be vented the anger that must be restrained against external enemies.

It is instructive to compare the treatment of the Jews in Germany with that of the "Kulaks" (that is, well-to-do peasants) in Russia. The Kulaks, by standing in the way of rural collectivization, were an obstacle to the Government's economic plans: they also provided a convenient scapegoat for any failures that might occur. Their persecution was in some ways almost as horrifying as that of the Jews. But at least it was not justified on false grounds of mysticism or pseudo-science. Their existence obstructed something which was of the essence of Communist planning, and they had to submit or be killed or expelled. The Jews could not even submit; because a false ideal of race had been erected to cloak the economic and psychological motives of the regime; they could only suffer at home, while some few have succeeded in going into exile abroad.

Culture, not "race," is, again, the crux of the American problem. The danger was that the American tradition might not suffice to absorb the vast body of alien ideas pouring into the country with the immigrant hosts, that the national melting-pot might fail to perform its office, and might crack or explode. When immigrants came in small numbers they could be, and were, absorbed, from whatever part of Europe they chanced to hail, and in at most two generations they

became an integral part of the American nation. Their
Alpine or Mediterranean elements stood in the way of the
process no more than their previous Czech or Italian
nationality. It was the size of the blocks of alien culture to
be assimilated which constituted the problem.

Racialism is a Myth

So long as nationalist ideas, even in modified form, continue to dominate the world scene, the large-scale segregation
of areas, each developing its own general type of culture,
may be the policy to pursue. If unrestricted immigration
seems likely to upset such a policy, restriction is justifiable,
as with Asiatic races in Australia and the United States.
But do not let us in such cases make it a question of "race,"
or become mystical on the subject, or justify ourselves on
false biological grounds.

The violent racialism to be found in Europe to-day is a
symptom of Europe's exaggerated nationalism: it is an
attempt to justify nationalism on a non-nationalist basis,
to find a basis in science for ideas and policies which are
generated internally by a particular economic and political
system, have real relevance only in reference to that system,
and have nothing to do with science. The cure for the racial
mythology, with its accompanying self-exaltation and persecution, which now besets Europe is a reorientation of
the nationalist ideal, and, in the practical sphere, an abandon-
ment of claims by nations to absolute sovereign rights.
Science and the scientific spirit are in duty bound to point
out the biological realities of the ethnic situation, and to
refuse to lend sanction to the "racial" absurdities and the
"racial" horrors perpetrated in the name of science. Racialism is a myth, and a dangerous myth. It is a cloak for selfish
economic aims which in their uncloaked nakedness would
look ugly enough. And it is not scientifically grounded.
The essence of science is the appeal to fact, and all the facts
are against the existence in modern Europe of anything in
the nature of separate human "races."

EDUCATION AS A SOCIAL FUNCTION

SCIENCE can concern itself with education not merely in regard to the scientific content of formal education or to the inculcation of scientific method and of the scientific attitude in general, but by considering education itself as a subject for scientific treatment, as a function of human social existence. In such a treatment two contrasted approaches can be made: from the point of view of society as a whole, and from that of its component individuals.

From the first point of view, education is the function by virtue of which the social tradition, both in its general and in its specialized aspects, is reproduced and enabled to evolve. It includes the transmission of a common language, of a common minimum basis of knowledge and skill; of the common traditions and ideals of society, and of certain norms of behavior. It further includes the transmission, via limited minorities, of specialized skills and techniques, craft and professional, and of certain general aspects of tradition via special élites. So from another angle education may be said to concern itself with the training of three sections within society—the élites, the specialists, and the residual mass.

The chief changes in educational theory which have emerged in the last half-century can be broadly summed up as follows: First, an increased emphasis on the evolutionary or change-facilitating function of education as against its conservative or change-resisting function. Secondly, and intimately connected with the first point, increased concern with the future, and with the possibility of approximation to ideal but scientific standards; and obversely a decreased concern with the past and with the imposition of ideal but non-scientific (philosophical or religious) standards derived from the past. Thirdly, a decreased stress on the rigid normative function of education, which aims at imposing, as early

223

as possible in life, certain orthodox patterns of thought, morality, and behaviour; and conversely an increased stress on its liberating function, through the encouragement of the scientific spirit, of individual thought and development, and of independence of action. Fourthly, recognition of the need, in any developed democratic society, for education to help in providing a high degree of social stimulation and social self-consciousness. Fifthly, recognition of a sane relativity as against a sham universality, of the fact that education is not only inevitably conditioned by the limitations of time and place but should be consciously related to the needs of the particular society of which it is a function.

In primitive societies such education as exists is in the form of a kind of apprenticeship to prepare boys and girls for adult tribal life, and is conveyed through ritual and legend. This is essentially static and conservative, subserving the reproduction of the traditional pattern; the evolutionary aspect of education, involving variation in the pattern transmitted, is accidental and slow. With the emergence of a class structure in society the general aspect of education alters. The stress then falls on the specialized education of an élite, whether that élite be itself the repository of power, as in ancient Egypt, or the favoured servant of the governing class, as in early medieval times.

The late Middle Ages marked the beginning of a new era. The invention of printing and other aids to the dissemination of knowledge made inevitable the gradual spread of mass education, while the growth of science and technology and of the scientific outlook not only made this mass education desirable in the intesests of efficiency, but stimulated the evolutionary function of education. We are now entering on a further phase, in which a highly integrated and self-conscious society is the aim, and in which therefore mass education must not only attain a much higher level, but the educational system must itself be fully unified and deliberately integrated as closely as possible with the life of society. Variation from the previous norm is becoming regarded as something to be consciously planned.

Coming down to the particular, we may remind ourselves of the chief social characteristics of education in the phase from which the Western world is now emerging. The first striking fact was the class duality of the system. Long-continued education was confined to a small minority, and designed to train a ruling class together with its necessary appendages and agents—the administrators and civil servants, the clergy, and the learned professions. Mass education, on the other hand, ended in early adolescence, and was designed to transmit the elementary skills of reading, writing, and arithmetical calculation necessary to carry on an industrial society, the modicum of historical and cultural education necessary to transmit a patriotic tradition of the nationalist type, and a smattering of the facts of nature. Specialized skills below the professional level were catered for by a combination of apprenticeship and an increasing volume of technical education, this latter being regarded as somehow inferior to education based on the humanities, and provided by the public schools and universities.

There was also an ideological duality, in respect of religion. Much pioneering work in mass education had been undertaken by religious bodies, partly from altruistic motives, partly to increase the influence of a particular church, and partly to introduce a religious and moral buffer against popular discontent with the glaring inequalities of the social system and the often shocking social conditions. This has influenced our educational system to this day, so that our elementary schools still consist in approximately equal numbers of provided schools wholly under public authority, and of non-provided schools, receiving grants from the State but belonging to various religious bodies.

As a result of this class basis the normative functions of education were (and are still) dispersed, and carried out by a patchwork of agencies. In regard to mass education the normative function remained largely in the hands of religious bodies, either in the non-provided schools or by way of Sunday schools, bible classes, and the like. In regard to the governing classes a strong normative influence was intro-

duced in the new public school tradition initiated by Arnold
at Rugby. In addition, the Church of England had at the
outset a monopoly of religious influence in public school
and university education, a monopoly which has been only
gradually and partially broken down.

Throughout this period education has been predominantly conservative in its social function. The emphasis has
been mainly on the past. There has been an intensive fostering of old-established tradition, support for existing prestige
and status, suspicion of new ideas, and resistance to new
methods. The long-continued education of the governing
classes has always pretended to universality. In point of fact,
it has confined itself largely to those portions of the past
which had contributed to the establishment of our own
tradition; but universality has been a deliberate aim. This
is exemplified in the emphasis at the older universities on
pure philosophy, and, once science had forced its way into
the curriculum, on pure science. Any relativist theory of
education has been frowned upon, though actually the
urgent needs of society have compelled functional education
at many points—highly specialized departments of science,
even of applied science, especially in provincial universities;
organizations like the Indian Institute at Oxford; and so
forth.

The need for providing the trained élites of society will
remain; but the nineteenth-century method of expensive
public school and university education cannot continue to
be tolerated in a democratic society, and in any case is
destined to break down as a result of the incidence of high
taxation on the wealthier classes.

More change has occurred in the universities than in the
schools; the latter have in very considerable measure been
thrown open to the less well-to-do. But the channel of
approach to them is through a highly competitive scholarship system, and is both over-intellectual and over-specialized,
with the result that the average of the young men and
women who reach the university on merit instead of on
money, are, in the view of many of those responsible for

them during their undergraduate career, in many ways far below the standard to be expected of an élite—in all-round character and interests, in intellectual initiative, and even in general education.

This can be partly remedied by amending the method of selection—by reducing the almost ludicrously high specialist standards demanded of candidates for scholarships, by laying more stress on general knowledge and varied interests, and by adding other criteria of selection to the examination tests. In part, however, this state of affairs is the result of unsuitable background, and here the universities are dependent on the schools. The remedy is surely, not to talk about abolishing the public schools or keeping those in difficulties alive by a bare minimum of State intervention, but to bring the public schools into the sphere of the national system, and to use them as training grounds for a certain type of élite (a functional élite based on merit and ability instead of a class élite based on property and privilege) for whom the corporate spirit of residential education is considered helpful.

This should help toward providing both background and backbone for the potential university student of poor family, who is now forced to overwork and over-specialize at the expense of health, character, and all-round interests. But the public school need not and certainly should not be the only channel of approach to the universities. No bar should be laid on candidates from the other secondary schools. A thorough overhaul of technical education is also required. It has been suggested in various quarters that types of technical school should be multiplied—that, for instance, building and agriculture, as well as industry and art, should be catered for. What is more important is that the whole status and prestige of the technical school should be raised, and the quality of the general educational background which it provides should be improved. There will then be a number of co-ordinate and equal channels of secondary-stage education.

There is further general agreement that education of some

sort should be universal up to 18 for those not taking a whole-time secondary education. The precise form of this requires to be worked out, but the facilities provided will, we may hope, be linked up with the various youth training and youth service organizations which are now assuming such importance.

With regard to the universities two main reforms seem indicated. One is the adoption of some system whereby students can move more freely from one university to another without impairing their chances of a degree, the other a closer linkage of our own university system with that of other countries. Approximation in general educational policy, increased facilities for visiting research workers of all ages, exchange of teaching and student personnel—all are needed. This in its turn has two facets, the international and the imperial. Internationally, while the utmost should be done to continue and extend the exchange of students, staff, and ideas between our universities and those of other continents, and especially of the United States, Europe will present a special and urgent need, for it is largely through education that we can expect to nourish the tender plant of super-national European patriotism. Naturally this European patriotism cannot and should not supplant national patriotisms; but its growth is indispensable to the future peace and progress of the European Continent. Higher education is bound to play an important role in the process, and we in this country must be on the alert and be prepared to take a position of leadership in providing a truly European system of universities for our Continent.

There are other international aspects of higher education to be considered. Among the most important of these will be the establishment of an international staff college to train administrators, both general and with specialist qualifications, for international work, whether in Europe, in the colonies, or elsewhere. Only so can we expect to, provide the staff necessary to carry on all the complicated supranational business of the world. The League of Nations secretariat and the I.L.O. have demonstrated that solidarity, standards, and *esprit de corps* can be produced relatively quickly in an international body; it is for an international staff college to add deliberate and specialized international training. There are many other international fields for education, such as the control of textbooks in the interests of international amity and general social development; but we cannot deal with them here.

On the imperial side, a great deal could be done toward bringing all institutions of higher education and research into a more unified system—by exchanges of teaching and research personnel, by special institutes at home, by ensuring that colonial colleges and universities should enjoy a higher status in their communities, and so on. A given expenditure from the Colonial Development Fund would probably go farther and achieve more striking results in fostering a unified imperial (not imperialist!) system of higher education than in any other field.

So far I have spoken of certain trends and adjustments in our educational system. But a more general problem remains, that of adapting the system as a whole to new tasks necessitated by the recent trends and promises of our type of society.

Education must be part of the mirror in which society may see itself entire. It is also becoming, to change the metaphor, the most important part of the apparatus by which society projects itself into the future. There was a time when popular education was conceived of as having two main functions—to teach the poor to be contented with their station in life, while equipping them with the three R's and those other rudiments of learning necessary to fit them for their place in a primitive industrial or palaeotechnic economy. This is, of course, an over-simplification. It was tempered by the sincere desire of many public-spirited people to make all the benefits of culture available to the masses. But culture was conceived of in terms of the very selective culture adapted to the needs and ideals of the leisured and professional classes in a highly stratified community; and in any case such movements only touched a small fraction of the working classes. In recent decades this conception has been considerably modified, but the dual system of education is still in being, and the class stratification of nineteenth-century Britain has left a strong impression on our twentieth-century system of education.

Meanwhile, quite new problems have now arisen. The technological advances of the two decades between the two world wars have altered the nature of power in the sense in which the term is used in international politics. It is no longer sufficient to be able to equip hastily raised conscript armies with rifles and bayonets, stiffen them with professional soldiers and artillery, and rely on a wave of jingo patriotism for public support. To-day successful war depends on vast industrial potential; and this must be backed, not only by high technical skill and the ability to ensure the supply of key raw materials from many parts of the world, but also by the active allegiance of the rank and file of the nation, on whom depend both the high-speed production of munitions and the maintenance of supplies and services. For this, simple patriotism is not enough: intelligent and willing co-operation is necessary. The mass of working men and women must feel themselves an integral part of a united society, not primarily as the "working classes" with interests in basic opposition to those of other classes. For this an obvious pre-requisite is a unified educational system, with high standards, and aiming at what Sir Stephen Tallents has called the Projection of England—in this case its projection into the minds of the rising generation.

But we are now learning that a purely national point of view is inadequate to present conditions: it is necessary to have an international as well as a national point of view, a world consciousness into which our set of national feelings and ideas (though these still remain of the utmost importance) can be fitted. Our own country's history and destiny must be set in a more general framework, and for this a further revision of our educational system, notably in regard

to text-books, as well as to the inclusion of certain new subjects, is required. Our education must become more closely
and more consciously related to the needs and possibilities
of our country at this particular time and in relation to the
rest of the world. It must give up the pretence of being based
on absolute or universal cultural values, and must abandon
the false and inadequate utilitarianism which sees in education solely or mainly a method for securing a job or doing
a job better.

It is a general rule, so general that we may almost call it
a law of history, that threatened interests and institutions
defend themselves with increasing vigour until a very late
stage in the process of their decay or supersession. Now such
a pattern of education as is here outlined involves a conception of society that threatens many various institutions
which have been so powerful in the immediate past that
they still have considerable reserves of power. The over-
privileged classes, the rentier-gentleman class, and in general
what is crudely described as the "old school tie" influence
in Government, business, and the professions, see their
privileges threatened—and not merely their material privileges, but, perhaps more important, their privileges of
prestige, their claim as a class to respect or even to subser-
vience. The capitalist class, whether engaged in large-scale
monopoly capitalism or in small-scale business, see themselves
threatened in a planned society with increasing control by
the State and increasing competition from public bodies and
co-operative agencies. The Churches, in part because tied
up with the old system, in part because their theological
basis is no longer acceptable to a large and increasing section
of the people, feel themselves threatened by the impending
shifts in our class system and still more by the rise of an outlook more concerned with social planning for this-worldly
improvement than with individual concern for other-worldly
salvation.

They will, all of them, resist the transformation of our
educational outlook. Those who uphold the relativist view of
education as a socially adapted function will increasingly

be denounced as vandals, denying to the people access to the full universality of culture, while the advocates of scientific planning will be told that they are undermining individuality and initiative. Those who advocate a more international background will be accused of lack of patriotism, and those who look for an adjustment of the Churches' theological outlook and institutional basis to modern conditions will be branded as immoral and anti-religious. Such accusations are a measure of the fear which the vested interests concerned are feeling, and can all in the long run be adequately met by a rational presentation of the facts. What we must be on our guard against are attempts at turning the clock back in educational practice—not merely because turning the clock back means delay and waste of time and energy but because of the danger of introducing unreality into our educational system.

An educational system properly planned as a social function, in close relation with contemporary social needs and trends, and with the aspirations, conscious and unconscious, of the society which it is designed to serve, will be a powerful aid toward social unification, social self-consciousness, and social advance. The converse is also true; an educational system which is seriously unrelated to the society in which it is attempting to function will hinder social unification and advance. What is more, this lack of social relation will recoil back on to the educational system itself, and will invest it with a sense of unreality which will cause the majority of boys and girls to look askance at the education provided for them.

This applies in two main fields—that of ideas and that of material conditions. Let me take two examples. Attempts to introduce the children of working-class families to a so-called universal or standard culture, when this is essentially a cultural of the leisured classes in past epochs, and there is scarcely a trace of a living culture in their own social environment, are doomed to failure. Apart from a few unusual individuals, and some temporary enthusiasts, children tend, by a perfectly healthy reaction, to reject contact with this

sort of culture as having no vital meaning either for themselves or for the communities of which they form part. It
becomes looked on as something highbrow and unreal, to
be dropped as soon as school days are over, or at least as
something to be kept to oneself, something to be rather
ashamed of, when brought face to face with the prevailing
standards and outlook of the hard and ugly industrial world.
The values accepted inside the school do not correspond
with those of the surrounding world; and not unnaturally
the world's values generally prove the stronger.

In such a case, the chief movement toward relating education and society must come from the side of society. On the
other hand, a considerable amount can be done within the
educational system; more attention can be paid to contemporary culture, to self-expression and self-development by doing
things rather than merely by learning about them and being
told what ought to be appreciated. But the main emphasis
must be on the social environment. It is here that adult
education, enlightened town and country planning, and
deliberate encouragement by the State and local authorities
of living art, music, drama, and all other branches of cultural
life, must be called on to do most of the bridging of the gap.
Nor must we forget that purely material considerations
weigh heavily. Until social security is a reality, and the
bulk of the population is guaranteed freedom from fear and
want, from ill-health and constant anxiety about the future,
they cannot be expected to display much interest either in the
masterpieces of the past or the cultural movements of the
present. The environment must be related to the needs of
the school every whit as much as the school and the education it provides are related to the needs of the society which
provides its environment.

That is one example. Another comes from the field of
religion. Of recent months the religious organizations of this
country have been making a strong bid for a renewal of
their influence in education. This has been embodied in a
manifesto issued by the Archbishops of Canterbury, York,
and Wales, with the concurrence of certain Free Church

Leaders. The manifesto comprises five points concerning the teaching of the Christian faith in schools, which they desire to see incorporated in the law of the land. In brief, while urging that religious instruction shall be in the hands of "teachers willing and competent to give it," they ask that religious knowledge shall be promoted to the status of an optional subject for the teacher's certificate, that religious instruction shall come under official inspection, that religious teaching may be given at any hour, and that the school day shall open with an "act of worship." There are also rumours abroad of a demand that non-provided schools shall be eligible for full grant, instead of the present 50 per cent. of their expenses. Quite apart from the fact that these points are bound to reawaken most of the bitter controversies of the past, the strategy of attempting to enforce a particular form of religious belief by legislaion, and of directing the attack upon children instead of upon the adult population, seems seriously mistaken.

If education is to be truly a function of society it should be given the vigour which springs from unity. There are at the moment two dualities in our educational system— one created by the class-cleavage between rich and poor, the other by the ideological cleavage between religious bodies and society as a whole. Only by abolishing both cleavages can we achieve that unified (but diversified) system which we need.

It would cost less in the long run for public authorities to buy out all the non-provided schools than to continue paying full grants for an indefinite period, and the essential step of unifying all the elementary schools would have been taken.

The other demand is even more obviously to be resisted by those who look forward to an educational system which shall play a really vigorous part in vitalizing society and projecting its ideals into the future. It is a fact, which many may deplore but which remains obstinately a fact, that the interest of the people of this country in orthodox Christianity, of whatever complexion, has enormously declined during the last few decades. The Christian ethic and doctrine have played an essential role in shaping our civilization; but there are unmistakable signs that they no longer satisfy our modern societies, and that some new formulation, both in the moral and the intellectual field, is becoming urgent if we are to reach a common foundation of thought and values for our national life. The religious revival we hear about at the moment is clearly a temporary phenomenon, of a sort familiar to all sociologists, due to war emotionalism. It has been accompanied by a much larger revival of non-religious superstitions, such as astrology.

In such circumstances, the insistence on religious observances in schools when religious influence is declining in the world outside will recoil on the heads of its proponents. Children are infallible detectors of unreality. As with culture, they will feel the contrast between the artificial religious atmosphere inside the school and the irreligious or indifferent atmosphere outside. This will in the long run promote in most of them an even more suspicious or even hostile attitude to orthodox religion than they would otherwise have acquired. But the mischief does not end here. A sense of unreality attaching to one portion of formal education tends inevitably to spread to the remainder. The introduction of more religious teaching and observance into the schools at this particular juncture will seriously hinder the development of an educational system which is to be an effective and organic function of our general social life.

The remedy again lies outside the schools. The religious impulse is a strong and persistent force in human life. But it is a complex impulse, differing radically in emphasis and aim from age to age as well as between one type of individual and another; and the doctrinal ritual and institutional forms in which it expresses itself are even more protean. We have witnessed the rise of two movements to which we must give at least the title of pseudo-religions—the Nazi and the Communist systems. It would appear of real importance that the existing democratic countries should evolve their own characteristic and powerful brand of religious impulse and means for its expression. This will not be achieved by a return to the traditional past. The Christian ethic and Christian doctrine, though they have left an indelible mark on our Western civilization in their insistence on the overriding value of the individual personality, on the necessity for sacrifice, and in many other ways, are no longer either a primary or an essential part of its framework. New attitudes, new values, new needs have come into being.

It is incumbent upon the Churches to recast their theologies in forms acceptable to the new phase of the Western world, and to readjust their social and ethical policies in relation to the needs of the new type of society which is in process of being born. If they attempt this with sincerity, it is incumbent upon society to meet them half-way. If this should be accomplished, organized religion in some new and at present unguessable form will come alive again as a social function, and could then rightly claim to have an important place in that other social function that we call education.

The approach to education from the individual end must also be considered. What has science to say on this? One cannot, of course, consider the individual in the abstract, but only as a member of a particular society. The question then is a double one: how can individuality be developed to the fullest pitch in our type of society, and how can the development of the individual be made to serve social ends to the fullest extent?

Recent developments in psychology and their educational applications have radically altered our approach. I am not referring only to psycho-analysis and the theory of repression and of the unconscious; we must also take account of the modern swing away from the over-emphasis on reason and the intellectual functions of the mind, to a system in which emotional factors and creative activity are given their due weight. There are also the numerous studies, anthropological and other, in social psychology, which have demonstrated the strength of social conditioning.

The concepts of repression and of the unconscious, which we owe primarily to Freud (whether or no we adopt an orthodox Freudian point of view), are cardinal and basic to the modern revolution of our ideas on individual education. In what follows I shall use the term mental energy in the broad popular sense, as denoting the driving forces of the psyche, emotional as well as intellectual, the capacity of the mind for getting work done, whether in the acquisition of knowledge or in the control and guidance of action.[1]

The essential implication of modern psychology is that through deep conflict an appreciable quantity of mental energy is either locked up and wasted, or distorted. Much of it is wholly bound, internally and at a low level, instead of being free and available for external or higher mental functions. A further quantity is bound in another sense by being organized, also at a low level, in such a way as to distort activity either into destructive instead of constructive channels, or into escape-fantasies instead of being related to reality.

The Central problem of individual education can thus no longer be regarded as intellectual; it is a deep-emotional one, and consists in the adjustment of conflict and the abolition of repression so as to make available the greatest quantity of mental energy for the most fruitful activities. This statement needs amplification. Repression, in the technical psychological sense, can be abolished, but conflict cannot. Man, it should be remembered, is the only organism habitually subjected to psychological conflict. In animals conflict is normally obviated by an all-or-nothing functioning of reflexes and instincts or drives, the throwing into action of one being

---

[1] Though perfectly aware that it is unscientific to employ the term *energy* in a wholly different sense from the sense in which it is used in the physical sciences, I shall do so because of the lack of any better term which is generally agreed upon. *Libido* is the nearest to such a term, but its use implies complete acceptance of orthodox psychoanalytic theory and has certain unsatisfactory connotations.

automatically accompanied, save in exceptional circumstances, by the throwing out of its competitors by a process
of inhibition.

In adult man conflicting impulses can be simultaneously
present in consciousness, and the resultant conflict can be
resolved consciously in the light of experience and reason.
This is impossible in the infant, who lacks the necessary
experience. Biologically speaking, repression thus appears
to be a device for preventing conflict in the early stages of
human existence, when it would have a disastrous effect.
The various "complexes" described by psychologists, and
the general structure of the psyche as adumbrated in the
Freudian scheme of ego, super-ego, and elements of the id
related by repression to the super-ego, are permanent or
semi-permanent resultants of this infantile adaptation carried
on into adult life.

It may be possible for a few special souls, or by means of
a special psychological technique, to abolish this primitive
structural pattern of the psyche and to unite super-ego, ego,
and id in a single and integrated entity; but, for the time
being at any rate, this is impossible for the majority of human
beings. What is possible, however, is to modify this primitive
psychical morphology into something less wasteful for the
purposes of adult human existence. This can be accomplished by minimizing the intensity and reducing the number of repressions in early life, and by substituting so far as
possible conscious and rational suppression for unconscious
and irrational repression as a means for the resolution of
conflicts, old and new alike.

There is a general as well as a special approach to this
question. The general attack will consist in relating the
whole subject of ethics to scientific fact and method, as has
recently been attempted by Dr. Waddington in *Nature*
(1941, vol. 148, p. 270). Any system of ethics is the consciously formulated rationalization of a much larger system
of compulsions and compulsive prohibitions, to which we
may give the Freudian label of super-ego. This super-ego
system, though essentially irrational and formed by the

action of unconscious mental forces, is not arbitrary, but is related to the facts of the external world through individual experience, largely at a very early age.

We must also take into account the extraordinary differences between the ethical systems of different human societies. The fact that actions that are regarded with the utmost horror in one place or time are in another community or another century accepted as moral duties—this apparent interchangeability of ethical black and white has often given rise to a resigned acceptance of complete relativism and subjectivism in ethics and a denial of the possibility of general ethical standards. But the scientific approach enables us to discern that these differences in ethical systems can be partly related to the social and material environment of the society in question, partly explained as "accidental" divergences of the sort which we find also in biological evolution among small and isolated groups. Further, the adoption of the evolutionary point of view at once makes it clear that we cannot expect to set up ethical standards which are either universal or complete. Ethics are part of the adjustment between man and his environment (of which the social environment comes to constitute an increasingly important fraction); thus ethical standards not only inevitably change with changing conditions, but the idea of change, or rather of certain directions of change, must itself become part of our ethical system.

Perhaps the most important contribution of natural science to general thought, after its demonstration of the regularity of all natural processes, and that they are in large measure both intelligible and controllable, is the demonstration of progress as an evolutionary fact. Biological progress existed before man, but man is now the sole repository of future possibilities of progress; further, progress is neither universal nor necessary, but merely one possibility among many. We can therefore say that there do exist general ethical standards, but that these are standards of direction, not absolute standards in the old static sense.

The ethical problem regarded from the scientific standpoint thus largely resolves itself into this question: How can the unconscious compulsions of very early life, which are generated primarily in relation to the infant's family circle and to the control of its biological functions, be rendered as little harmful as possible; and how can they be subsequently related, in a more conscious way, to the wider concepts of society and of evolutionary progress? As Waddington well puts it, "a child learns at its mother's knee that aggression must be controlled; and it learns a little later that taunting its younger brother's weakness is a form of aggression, but when does it learn that adopting an unscientific attitude to the social problem of nutrition is also aggression," and therefore unethical? The same applies to war and many other activities.

The problem is clearly one of the greatest complexity and difficulty, but the fact that it has at last been scientifically formulated (which has only become possible in the last few decades) is itself extremely important. One thing at least is clear, that it must be approached from the social as well as the individual angle. The more frustration or unmerited cruelty or hardship an individual meets with owing to the social conditions into which he is born, the more likely are his conscious ethical principles liable to be distorted in an undesirable way, and also to be overriden by undesirable unconscious compulsions, whether of aggression or of escape. What is more, so much of the emotional-ethical structure is laid down in infancy in relation to the child's family circle, that the distortions and repressions of one generation have a strong tendency to perpetuate themselves, though often in altered form, in the next. Educated and unfrustrated parents are a necessary part of the social mechanism for producing educated and unfrustrated children.

The problem of getting rid of undesirable repressions can also be attacked by specific methods. Of these, the method of encouraging self-expression through creative activity which is both free and self-disciplined, is probably the most important. Creative activity can take many forms, from play to poetry, from mud-pies to acting; it can and should be encouraged from the earliest years. It has two related but distinct functions. It may help to rid the child of haunting repressions that are inhibiting its healthy development. But expression can be normative as well as creative. It can help the child to find outlets for itself, and so avoid new frustrations; it can also in many cases relate the individual to larger social groups or to comprehensive ideas, thus providing channels for sublimation and helping the narrow, irrational, and unconscious emotional-ethical system of infancy to develop into the broader, more rational and more conscious system demanded by adult existence. I have no doubt that both the normative and the therapeutic possibilities of creative activity should be given a much larger part to play in our educational system.

Another special problem is that of the adolescent, and in particular the sensitive and gifted adolescent. At the moment, we do our best to make the worst out of our human material by ending mass education at 14 or 15, and demanding of the majority of our children that they shall begin facing the world and its problems in that most difficult and critical of all periods of life, early adolescence. The raising of the school-leaving age to 16 and the provision of part-time education up to 18 are probably more important on this than on any other account. Meanwhile, there is the special problem of the education of the élite. One of the major defects of the world to-day is the dearth of men of imagination, intellect, and sensibility in high places. In the majority of cases, such men seem to lack the drive and confidence needed for public life. The result is that the tough and blatant, the unimaginative, or the pushing types too often rise to the top. There are exceptions, of course—Dr. Nansen and Field-Marshal Smuts spring to the mind—but they are all too rare. In many cases it is during adolescence that the diffidence of self-distrust of the gifted but sensitive type either originates or becomes firmly established.

Can this unfortunate state of affairs be remedied? There is a good deal of evidence that it can, by means of measures deliberately designed for the purpose. First comes the need for confidence in one's physical capacities; then the need for confidence in one's capacity for perservance and, in the process of success, for overcoming the fear of failure and of being found wanting; and finally the need for feeling one-self useful, wanted, appreciated.

Methods such as the Scout training and the revised County Badge scheme, with its "projects" as well as its all-round athletic tests and its expedition tests, go a long way towards laying the foundations of the necessary psycho-physical self-reliance. The all-round physical requirements of the latter go a long way toward producing the desired result, and the individual initiative and patience demanded by a good project provide a superstructure. Also, it seems clear that some form of service, in which the adolescent is not playing at being grown-up, but is (and knows that he is) being useful to the community, is also required.

Meanwhile, to define the problem is the first step toward solving it. A scientific survey of education as a social function helps us to define the dynamic function now required of education as a transmitter of an evolving tradition; the need for education to contribute to social self-awareness and cultural unity; its importance in training an élite which shall be efficient and truly representative of the country as a whole; the importance of creative work and self-expression and of other special methods for overcoming repression and adolescent hyper-sensitiveness; the necessity of adjusting social conditions to educational ideals and practice, and vice versa. These are in the long run much more important than questions of curriculum or administration, however necessary and urgent.